Purchased on May 10, 199
on our visit to
Museo del Prado
Madrid, Spain

c Alice Goulding
Ellie Ancin
Ed Ancin

ILLUSTRATED GUIDE

P. LOPEZ DE OSABA
W. BRAUNFELS
L. DUSSLER
W. SAUERLÄNDER

THE PRADO MUSEUM

SERIE MINOR

 CERO OCHO EDITIONS

Printed in offset by Gráficas Cuenca; Hnos. Valdés, 28; Cuenca.
Photocomposition: Gráficas Cuenca.
Cover by Gustavo Torner.
Published: Cero Ocho Editions.
® Cero Ocho Editions.
Photographs: ® Copyright - Prado Museum - Madrid. All rights reserved. Complete or partial
    reproduction prohibited.
Translations: From the Spanish and German texts by Susanne Felkau.
ISBN: 84-85892-01-1.
Legal Deposit: CU-109-1981.

OPENING HOURS:

VILLANUEVA BUILDING.
MONDAY TO
SATURDAY: 10 A.M. TO 6 P.M. (OCTOBER-MARCH).

OPENING HOURS:

VILLANUEVA BUILDING.
MONDAY TO SATURDAY: 10 A.M. TO 6 P.M. (ABRIL-SEPTEMBER).
                    10 A.M. TO 5 P.M. (OCTOBER-MARCH).
SUNDAYS AND HOLIDAYS: 10 A.M. TO 2 P.M.

ADMISSION:

VILLANUEVA BUILDING: 100 PTAS.

FREE ADMISSION (UPON PRESENTATION OF DOCUMENTATION) FOR TEACHERS, STUDENTS, WORKERS, SENIOR CITIZENS, AND OTHER AUTHORIZED PERSONS.

GROUP VISITS (MAX. 25 PERSONS) BY WRITTEN PETITION.

RESTAURANT AND CAFETERIA: UNDER CONSTRUCTION.

AUDIOVISUAL AND FILMS: UNDER INSTALLATION.
TELEPHONES: 230 34 39 - 468 09 50 - 230 62 04 - 230 91 14.

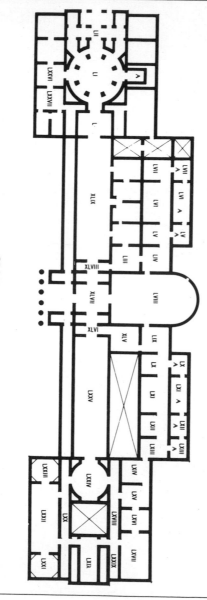

GROUND FLOOR

Maderuelo, 12thC - frescos.
ROOM: A

Information - Sales.
ROOM: LI

Library - Administration.
ROOMS: LXXVI, LXXVII

Spanish Painting, 15th-16thC.
ROOMS: L. XLIX AND XLVIII

Goya.
ROOMS: LVII A, LVIA, LV A, LVII, LVI, LV AND LIII.

France, 17thC.
ROOM: LIV

Area temporarily closed because of construction:
ROOMS: LX A, LX, LXI A, LXI, LXII A, LXII, LXIII A, LXIII, LXXV, LXXIX, LXXIV, LXIX, LXX, LXXIII, AND LXXI

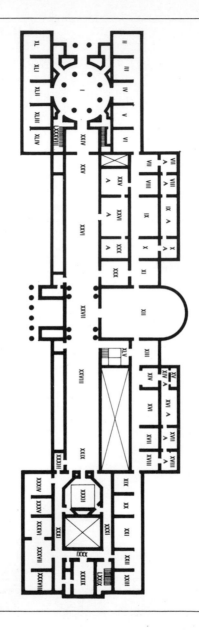

MAIN FLOOR

Italian Painting, 16thC.
- Raphael.
- Botticelli.
- Mantegna.
- Fra Angelico.
- A. del Sarto.
ROOMS: II, III, IV, V, AND VI.

Flemish Painting, 15th-16thC.
- Master of Flémalle.
- Van der Weyden.
- Bosco.
- Patinir.
- Dürer.
ROOMS: XL, XLI, XLII, XLIII, AND XLIV.

Spanish Painting, 17thC.
- Cano.
- Murillo.
ROOMS: XXIV, XXV, AND I.

Spanish Painting, 16thC.
- Sánchez Coello.
- El Greco.
- Ribera.
- Ribalta.
- Velázquez.
- Zurbarán.
ROOMS: XXV A, XXVI A, XXX A, AND XI.

Venetian Painting.
- Veronese.
- Tintoretto.
- Bassano.
- Giorgione.
- Titian.
ROOMS: VII A, VIII A, IX A, X A, VII VIII, IX, AND X.

Velázquez.
ROOM: XII.

Flemish Painting.
- Rubens.
- Van Dyck.
ROOMS: XXVI AND XXVII.

Rooms reserved for special exhibits:
ROOMS: XV, XIV A, XIV, XVI A, XVI, XVII A, XVII, XVIII A, AND XVIII.

Area closed for construction:
ROOMS: XXVIII, XXIX, XIX, XX, XXI, XXII, XXIII, XXXI, LXXIX, XXXII, XXXIX, XXXIV, XXXV, XXXVI, XXXVII, AND XXXVIII.

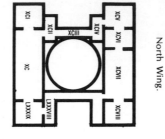

TOP FLOOR

North Wing.

Italian Painting.
NORTH WING.

Temporarily closed for construction.
SOUTH WING.

TOP FLOOR

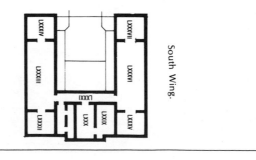

South Wing.

THE MUSEUM'S COLLECTIONS

P. LOPEZ DE OSABA

Taken as a whole and ignoring some extra pieces acquired by later fortunate measures, the magnificent collection of Spanish and foreign paintings in the Prado Museum has its origin in the collection of the Spanish Royal House. Beginning with Charles V, the Spanish monarchy developed an extraordinary eagerness in collecting paintings of the greatest contemporary artists. In the Alcázar of Madrid, altered according to the Emperor's wishes, exquisite pictures were assembled, the number of which gradually grew to enrich the artistic patrimony of the monarch. To these works were added the collections inherited from his aunt doña Margarita of Austria (widow of the Infante don Juan), and from Joanna the Mad and Philip the Fair; as well as the collection he inherited from his grandparents —the Catholic Queen left 460 paintings on canvas and panels when she died—, and that of Maximilian. Given the above, one can estimate the quality and quantity of the core of paintings which Madrazo estimated to be some 600 works. After Charles' V death at Yuste the collection was about to be dispersed by a public auction as, at that time, usually was done with these acquisitions of the Crown. Philipp II, however, who at an early age had demonstrated a refined esthetic taste was able to secure the whole pictorial oeuvre owned by his father. To this fund the acquisitions by Philip II himself as sponsor of Titian were added, furthermore the most valuable works of the Flemish School which, along with the Venetian School, was his favourite. By his passion for collecting paintings Philip left at his death actually three museums: the Alcázar in Madrid, the Escorial and the Pardo.

Philip III also bought his father's paintings when the latter died and acquired for himself the collection of the Prince of Mansfield in Flandes. The place where most paintings were concentrated during the reign of this monarch, el Pardo, had 355 works at his death, a number which was reduced by the calamitous fire in the palace en 1604.

The reign of Philip IV marks an undoubtable zenith of both Spanish painting and collecting. The King had an almost morbid for buying paintings, which is all the more admirable in a period when the finances went badly. During this reign Spanish painting reached unexpected heights. The King retained Diego Velázquez as court painter. It is curious that this apogee of Spanish painting took place when Spanish power was already in decline and that it followed almost a hundred years later the Renaissance peak of Spanish literature.

Apart from these two fundamental facts, Philip IV acquired major works from the public auctions of the unfortunate Charles I of England and of Rodrigo Calderón, Philip III's minister, who was beheaded at the beginning of the reign of Philip IV. When we add to this the purchases made by Velázquez on his second journey to Italy and the copies made by Rubens during his stay in Madrid on a diplomatic mission; the presents which the Count-Duke of Olivares forced the aristocracy to part with willingly or unwillingly, then it is no surprise that on the death of the monarch, the inventory in the Alcázar in Madrid counted 1547 paintings.

With Charles II begins a series of disastrous incidents which ruined a good part of these collections. First the tremendous fire in the Escorial in 1671; then, under the first of the Bourbons, Philip V, the terrible fire in the Alcázar in Madrid on Christmas night 1734. 537 paintings were lost forever in this fire.

In all fairness, the desire to acquire new paintings and to repair as far as possible the catastrophe caused by the fires was very great. However, the new acquisitions were not as fortunate as those made by previous monarchs. We owe the discovery of Murillo to Philip V and his second wife, Isabel de Farnesio. During their stay in Seville, they became so fond of his painting that they bought 29 of his works. These enhanced the royal collections and particulary their favourite project, the palace of La Granja.

Charles III finished building the new Palace in Madrid and had it decorated by Tiepolo and Mengs. The Palace was completed in 1774.

We also have to thank Charles III for the acquisitions of Spanish paintings which considerably broadened the scope of the royal collections. Like Philip IV, Charles IV disposed of a court painter of genius: Francisco de Goya. His works in the Prado are one of the greatest attractions to visitors by both their quality and their quantity.

The year 1808 was one of sad memories for Spain, not only because of political and social events, but also from an artistic standpoint. Destructions, dilapidations, fires, and robberies without limit were the tragic result of these bad events. Napoleon took from the official collections 50 paintings to his museum (works by el Greco, Ribera, Velázquez, Zurbarán, Cano, Murillo, Titian, Veronese, Raphael, Andrea del Sarto). Already during the Restoration it cost much toil to get them finally returned. What was never returned were the paintings and art treasures which the invading generals took with them on their withdrawal. It must be noted that the eagerness to collect paintings did not end with the exile of Charles IV. An inventory of 688 paintings was left on his death. Of these some fell to the lot of his son Ferdinand VII. Those were later incorporated into the collections of the museum that he built, which is today the Prado.

To this artistic treasure which was stored for centuries by the kings of Spain must be added important bequests (a detailed account is found in the official cataloque of the Prado Museum). Furthermore, the management of the Museum has always bee attentive to possible private sales and public auctions which in many cases have led to successful acquisitions. Particularly magnificent are the bequests by Ramón Errazu (1904); Pablo Bosch (1915); Pedro Fernández-Durán (1930); and Francisco de Asís Cambó (1940) and (1941).

Among the acquisitions made by the Museum the exceptional Antonello di Messina stands out as the most fortunate purchase in this century. It was acquired thanks to the tenacious perseverance of Xavier de Salas, the former subdirector of the Prado. The same is true of the beautiful Goya: Don Gaspar Melchor de Jovellanos.

BIBLIOGRAPHY

Madrazo, D. Pedro de: *"Viaje artístico de tres siglos por las colecciones de cuadros de los Reyes de España"*,1964.

Beroqui, D. Pedro: *"El Museo del Prado - Notas de su historia"*. Madrid, 1933.

Hempel de Lipschutz, Ilse: *"El despojo de las obras de arte en España durante la guerra de la Independencia"* en *"Arte Español"*, 1961.

Gaya Nuño, Juan Antonio: *"Historia del Museo del Prado"*, 1969.

Lafuente Ferrari, E.: *"El Museo del Prado"*. Madrid, 1968.

E. Pérez Sánchez, Alfonso: *"Pasado, presente y futuro del Museo del Prado"*. Madrid, 1977.

SPANISH PAINTING UNTIL EL GRECO

P. LOPEZ DE OSABA

A Vasari is missing in the history of Spanish painting. That is to say, an "artist chronicler" with love and discernment for painters and their work would have been invaluable to us. Of course, we know that not everything Vasari tells us about Italian painting can be accepted unequivocally, but even so, a chronicle of this kind would have been very useful to us.

Spain had a somewhat similar figure in Antonio Palomino. He lived, however, at the height of the 18thC and was influenced by the conviction that painting earlier than what we now call the Renaissance was a product of barbarism and therefore unworthy of even sketchy descriptions. Also in the 18thC another man of knowledge, Antonio Ponz, set out to see the Spanish artistic inheritance "in situ" (1772-1798). His eighteen volumes could have been an invaluable catalogue of what his eyes saw if only he had taken note of signatures, works, and places that would have shed light on many of the masters that today remain in the shadows. He did not do so because he shared Palomino's prejudices. Neither Giuseppe Martínez in his 16thC "discursos" nor Ceán who wrote his "Dictionary" at the transition from the 18thC to the 19thC brought light into a period which irrevocably, after so many calamities, must always remain obscure.

Whith Romanticism there was a re-discovery of Pre-Renaissance art, and attitudes changed. Appreciation of 15thC painting became the object of general and unparalleled interest. Today we see in that epoch an excess in which the Romantics found their own feelings expressed. But the fact is that this enthusiam contributed greatly to the increase in our knowledge about this period of painting. This view of the 15thC was also taken up in Spain, although with the usual delay. Thanks to the works of Pedro de Madrazo —An Artistic Journey Through Three Centuries of Collections of Paintings of the Kings of Spain (Barcelona 1884)— old inventories were brought to light. Even though they were administrative inventories they made obvious the love and respect Isabella of Castille had for painting, and they indicated the approximate number of works in her possession.

It is difficult to define exactly the characteristics of Spanish painting. Briefly and along general lines one can say with E. Lafuente Ferrari that Spanish art is always characterized by the following elements:

a) An energetic and virile way of creating; a certain seriousness which at times becomes disdain, coarseness, and an incredible lack of imagination tinged by a certain melancholy; an air and solemnity dominated by etiquette and composed forms. **b)** An almost reverential respect for beings and things. Usually, Spanish painters do not show details for their own sake, as Flemish painters do, but with a sense of profound honesty towards their existential individuality, evoking more than copying their essence. This gives us above all an unencumbered visual presence that is not idealized as might be true of the Italians. **c)** As a result of this orientation Spanish painting is inclined towards large scale and life size. It prefers in any event the man to the landscape. **d)** With rare exceptions the nude, therefore mythological subjects, have not been the strong point of Spanish painters. **e)** Finally, the tendency towards the pictorial over the linear, according to Wofflin's classic distinction, demonstrate an insecurity in the drawing that almost reaches the point of chronic weakness which can be seen even in the great masters.

The political insecurity and instability of Spain on the one hand, and the lack of wealth, that principal consumer of works of art, on the other, eliminated the possibility of artistic centers with their natural competition and rivalries that may, as they did in Italy, bring forth a generation of great masters in several states and cities that are thought of as small master works.

During the 14thC the Italian influence can be seen in its two main aspects: the Sienese School which came by way of the court at Avignon to the Catalan-Aragonese kingdom (Ferrer Bassa; Jaume y Pere Serra), and the Florentine School, which was centered in the Meseta of Spain, concretely in Toledo in the person of Gherardo di Jacopo Starnina and in Salamanca with Dello di Nicola or Nicholas the Florentine. This influence continued until the 15thC when Spain joined the decorative "international style". Parallel to this the way was opened for Flemish influence; one recalls the journey of Jan van Eyck to Portugal in 1428-29 on a diplomatic mission. Fernando Gallego (1466-67; 1507), Jaume Huguet (1414-15, 1487), Alejo Fernández (1475; 1545-46), Juan de Flandes (died 1519), Nicolás Francés and the great figure of Bartolomé Bermejo (between 1474 and 1495) are examples. After his stay in Urbino Pedro de Berruguete (died 1503) tried to combine the Flemish tradition he had been under befores his departure with the Italian ideas about composition from the Cuattrocento.

The 16thC is characterized by an inclination towards Italian painting, even when the Flemish tradition continued to be strong in Castille. There it continued until Philip II with the Dutchman Antonio Moro (1519-1576) and his influence on the Spanish portrait painters Sánchez Coello (1531-32; 1588) and Pantoja de la Cruz (1533-1608). Pedro Machuca's (died 1550) two panels in the Prado bring us an echo of the Renaissance movement that he experienced in Italy. His palace of Charles V in Granada is —as it has been said— the most beautiful example of Renaissance architecture outside of Italy. The echo of Leonardo's work in the pictorial art is seen clearly in the paintings of Fernando Yáñez (died 1531-36?).

At the end of the century one of the most illustrious figures of European painting arises: El Greco (1540-1614). Trained in Venice, perhaps under Titian, unconvinced by Roman mannerism, he found in Toledo and in the fervent Spanish religiosity —the spiritual exercises of Saint Ignatius, Saint Theresa of Jesus, and Tomás Luis Victoria— the perfect context to mold his "expressionistic" and delirious visions that make him the greatest spiritualist of western art.

BIBLIOGRAPHY

Angulo, D.: *"La pintura trecentista en Toledo"*, A.E.A.A., 1935.

Angulo Iñiguez: *"Pintura del Renacimiento"*, 16thC, *"Ars Hispaniae"*, XII, 1954.

Gudiol, Ricard, J.: *"Pintura del s. XV"*, *"Ars Hispaniae"*. Madrid, 1955.

Lafuente Ferrari, E.: *"Breve historia de la pintura española"*. Madrid, 1953.

Lafuente Ferrari, E.: *"El Museo del Prado. Del romántico al Greco"*. Madrid, 1965.

Mayer, A. L.: *"Geschichte der spanischen Malerei"*. Leipzig, 1922.

Post, Chandler R.: *"A History of Spanish Painting"*, vol. X, Cambridge (Mass.), 1950-58, 12 vols.

Sánchez-Cantón, F. J.: *"El Museo del Prado"*. Madrid, 1949.

MURALS FROM SAN BAUDELIO DE CASILLAS DE BERLANGA.

SOLDIER. Fresco transferred to canvas. From the second half of the 12thC. 2.90 × 1.34 m. The mural has been in the Prado since 1957. Of the series of then murals six are in the Prado. The artist is called the "Master from Berlanga" in order to distinguish him from the artist of the upper religious cycle, whom Messrs. Cook and Gudiol identify, because of the geographic proximity, with the master of Maderuelo.

THE HARE HUNT. Fresco transferred to canvas. From the second half of the 12thC. 1.85 × 3.60 m. The mural has been in the Prado since 1957 on deposit from the Metropolitan Museum of Art in New York. It was identified by Manuel Aníbal and Ramón Mélida in 1907. This painting and the previous one form part of one of the two "cycles" in the Mozarabic church of the beginning of the 11thC. The upper one is dedicated to the Life of Christ and the History of the Salvation of which the Prado does not have any example. The murals in the Museum belong to the lower cycle, with profane subjects of strong oriental inspiration, perhaps related to miniature works.

Such a cycle is most unusual and, according to Cook, it is one of the most extraordinary series of murals in all of western Europe.

MURALS FROM SAN BAUDELIO DE CASILLAS DE BERLANGA.

ELEPHANT. Fresco transferred to canvas. From the second half of the 12thC. 2.15 × 1.36 m. The mural has been in the Prado since 1957. Professor Post has seen Mozarabic influences and traces not only in this lower cycle, but also in the upper one. When the paintings were transported to the United States in 1926, they were acquired by the museums in Boston and Indianapolis, and by the Cloisters Museum in New York.

MURALS FROM THE HERMITAGE OF THE CROSS IN MADERUELO (Segovia).
THE CREATION OF ADAM AND THE ORIGINAL SIN. Fresco transferred to canvas in 1947. Semicircle.

MURALS FROM THE HERMITAGE OF THE CROSS IN MADERUELO.
CAIN AND ABEL PRESENT OFFERINGS TO THE LAMB INSERTED IN THE CROSS. Fresco transferred to canvas in 1947. Semicircle.

MURALS FROM THE HERMITAGE OF THE CROSS IN MADERUELO.
THE ADORATION BY A MAGUS OF THE VIRGIN WITH THE CHILD. Fresco transferred to canvas in 1947.

ANONYMOUS PAINTER FROM THE 14TH-15TH C.

VIRGIN WITH CHILD (No. 2707). 1.61 × 0.92 m. Pablo Bosch Besquest *(No. 75)*.

ANONYMOUS PAINTER FROM THE 15TH C.

ALTAR-PIECE OF ARCHBISHOP SANCHEZ DE ROJAS (No. 1321). Acquired by the Museum in 1929 from the church of San Román de Hornija (Zamora).

This work is a good example of the development of altar-pieces as ornamental objects introduced into Spain. We could easily attribute political significance to it. In the lowest central panel the Virgin and Child sit on a throne surrounded by angels with a saint on either side. She is placing the mitre on the head of Sancho de Rojas, who was first bishop of Palencia until 1415 and then cardinal of Toledo until his death in 1422. As protector of the Convent of San Benito in Valladolid he is presented to the Virgin by the founder of the order for whose convent this altar-piece was designed. To the right the Child is crowning a King. This can be no other than Ferdinand of Antequera who was elected king at the Compromise of Caspe in 1412. He was very close to Sancho de Rojas, who accompanied him during the campaign. Ferdinand, King of Aragon, was the son of John I of Castille, who died in 1416. The King is presented to the Child by a saint, who mus St. Domingo de Guzmán, the predecessor of Ferdinand. It is an act of manifest legitimization of power that comes from on high. The large panel from 1317 by Simone Martini of St. Luis of Tolosa, which is in the Naples museum, may be considered the first example in the west of this type. The elegantly drawn lines of this painting show the Tuscan influence on Castillian painting. This influence may have reached Spain through Gherardo di Jacopo Starnina, a master who worked in Toledo in the last quarter of the 14thC. He left a group of disciples whose work is centered in the murals of the Chapel of San Blas del Obispo Tenorio in the cathedral of Toledo. The altar-piece was removed in 1537 to be replaced by an altar-piece carved by Alonso Berruguete.

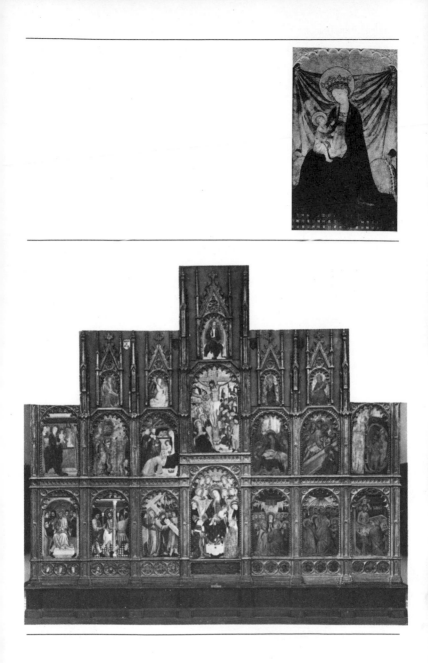

FERNANDO GALLEGO.

Worked from 1466/67 to 1507 in the kingdom of Castille and Leon. Clearly influenced by Flemish painting. Lit. Gaya Nuño, A., *"Fernando Gallego"*. Madrid, 1959.

THE PIETA, OR THE FIFTH ANGUISH (No. 2998). Wood 1.18 × 1.02 m. The painting was acquired from Mrs. Weibel (Madrid) in 1959 by the Ministry of National Education. The dramatic character of the image and the angularity of the folds in the clothes make us think of an early work that is close in time to the panel of the Calvary. The figure of Christ reminds us of the tremendous Castillian sculptures loaded with drama. The austere landscape is also a point that separates the painting from nordic pleasantness. Post and Lafuente rightly see a close relationship to the work of the Swiss Conrad Witz.

FERNANDO GALLEGO, 1466/67-1507.

THE CALVARY (No. 2997). Wood 0.92 × 0.83 m. The painting was bought from Mrs. Weibel in 1959 by the Ministry of National Education. Although Post thinks it a late work because of its perfect technique, the intense dramatization in it might justify an earlier dating. This may be true particulary if we think of how later works by the same artist have lost this tremendous character gaining a more human gentleness.

MISERERE MEI DIE

FERNADO · GALLEGS

FERNANDO GALLEGO, 1466/67-1507.

CHRIST GIVING BLESSINGS (No. 2647). Wood 1.69 × 1.32.

Painted before 1492. Bosch Bequest No. 15. The painting came to the Prado in 1915. It is the central panel in the altar-piece of St. Lawrence in Toro. It is a Spanish-Flemish version of the Pantocrator Tetramorphus. The panel is a consummate example of Flemish influence on Spanish painting in the 15thC. We do not know whether Fernando Gallego learned his craft in Flanders, but in any case, the study of first rate Flemish originals influenced and shaped his profound personality. The panel was commissioned by Pedro de Castilla and his wife Beatriz de Fonseca.

FERNANDO GALLEGO, 1466/67-1507.

THE MARTYRDOM OF ST. CATHERINE (No. 3039). Wood 1.25 × 1.09 m. The panel was bought in 1961 from Mr. Lucas in Madrid. It is a very beautiful and rare example of a nude in Spanish painting.

ANONYMOUS SPANISH PAINTER FROM THE 15TH CENTURY.

THE VIRGIN OF THE CATHOLIC MONARCHS (No. 1260). Wood 1.23 × 1.12 m. From the chapel of the Royal Chamber in the Convent of St. Thomas in Avila. It came to the Prado from the Trinidad Museum. It is a Spanish-Flemish work from about 1490.

The panel has more historic than artistic interest. Everything in it has been much discussed. From left to right: Ferdinand V with his firstborn son, John. Behind them, kneeling, Brother Thomas of Torquemada, the famous inquisitor. Standing, St. Thomas Aquinas. To the right, queen Isabella and her daughter Isabella (or Joanna?). Kneeling, behind, St. Peter Martyr Anglería (Anghiera), the Italian humanist and chronicler, bearing the attributes of St. Peter. Like the Sancho de Rojas altar-piece, this painting has a marked political significance. The Virgin and the Child accompanied by St. Thomas, the great theologian, and St. Dominic, the founder of the religious order, who was related to the reigning house, protect the royal family and its councellors.

JUAN DE FLANDES, 15TH-16TH CENTURY.

In 1469 Juan de Flandes worked for queen Isabella. One has tried to identify him with John Sallaert, the Flemish painter who worked in Ghent in 1480. He painted the altar-piece in the cathedral of Palencia which was commissioned in 1509. He died in that city about 1519. Lit. Bermejo, Elisa, *"Juan de Flandes".* Madrid, 1962.

THE PRAYER IN THE GARDEN OF GETHSEMANE (No. 2936). Wood 1.10 × 0.84 m. The painting was acquired in May 1952.

JUAN DE FLANDES, 15TH-16TH CENTURY.

THE RESURRECTION OF LAZARUS (No. 2935). Wood 1.10 × 0.84 m. Acquired in May 1952. The four panels in the Prado together with two more bought from Mr. Kress come from the church of St. Lazarus in Palencia. Without relinquishing his very important Flemish training, Juan de Flandes exhibits the stereotype of the Spanish character in his work, both in the severe backgrounds of nature and in the austere expressions of the people he depicts.

THE ASCENSION OF THE LORD (No. 2937). Wood 1.10 × 0.84 m. The painting was acquired in May 1952.

JAUME HUGUET.

Born in valls about 1415. He worked in Zaragoza and later in Barcelona where he died in 1492. He owned a large workshop and put out a considerable amount of work, particulary for the guilds who were his main clients. Lit. Ainaud de Lasarte, *"Juan Jaime Huguet"*. Madrid, 1955.

A PROPHET (No. 2683). Wood 0.30 × 0.26 m. Pablo Bosch Bequest No. 51.

This is a fragment of a predella in grisaille of an altar-piece done by the Master of Valls. The personal drawing, the elegance of the figures, and a certain melancholic aspect in the finely modeled portraits, all combine to make this fragment of Catalan painting a showpiece in the Museum. Huguet was one of the most prolific artists of the Barcelonan period 1448-92. This work, which was previously believed to be by the Master of Segovia, has now been attributed to Huguet by Gudiol and J. Ainaud.

BARTOLOME BERMEJO.

Bermejo was born in Córdoba. He worked in the Spanish Levant and Aragon from 1474 to 1495. Lit. Young, Eric, *"Bartolomé Bermejo"*. London, 1975.

ST. DOMINIC OF SILOS (No. 1323). Wood 2.42 × 1.30 m. The painting was commissioned on September 5, 1474 and was finished on November 17, 1477. It was collected by Saviron for the Archaeological Museum in 1869-71 and came to the Prado en 1920.

The signature of Bartolomé Bermejo, "Cordubensis", on the large panel of the Pietà of the Canon Desplá in the cathedral of Barcelona opened the way to the discovery of this great artist, one of the most important painters of the Spanish-Flemish current. The enormous panel in the Prado represents St. Dominic of Silos, the founder of the famous monastery in Burgos. It shows the enthronement of wisdom and holy authority with a clear and rigorous sense of order. The saint is seated in a pulpit and dressed in pontifical robes. He is expounding a text surrounded by the theological virtues (Faith, Hope, and Charity) and the cardinal virtues (Prudence, Justice, Fortitude and Temperance). The figure is painted with a richness of details and a fine sense of chiaroscuro which gives it the character of monumental relief. Notwithstanding the wealth of gold and filigree, the great face of the saint is the center of the painting; it forcefully dominates the whole scenario. The monumental size of the figure is already one of the marks which is going to prevail through the entire history of Spanish painting.

ANONYMOUS SPANISH PAINTER, from the second half of the 15thC.

ST. MICHAEL THE ARCHANGEL (No. 1326). Canvas attached to panel. 2.42×1.53 m. Acquired in 1924 from the St. Michael hospital in Zafra by the Museum Foundation.

This magnificent painting is the only one in the Prado from the primitive Andalusian School. As almost always is the case, it is not connected with a known master. The painting is a display of beautiful and impeccable technique. The chaotic world of vermin, monsters, demons, and angels holds an astonishing mobility. It is reminiscent of the fascinating world of Bosch. All this the master has made into a large background curtain that focuses attention on the life-size majestically elegant and perfectly natural figure of St. Michael. The exquisite care that is shown in color and pictorial effects such as the reflections in the cuirass were a great novelty at that time.

PEDRO BERRUGUETE, 1450?-1504.

Born in Paredes de Nava. In 1477 active at the court of Federico of Monte-feltro in Urbino. Trained in the Flemish-Castillian style came under the influence of the painting of the Quattrocento during his stay in Italy. Died in 1504. Lit. Angulo, D., *"Berruguete en Paredes de Nava"*. Barcelona, 1946.

ST. DOMINIC AND THE ALBIGENSIANS (No. 609). Wood 1.22 × 0.83 m. The painting originates from the Convent of St. Thomas in Avila. It came to the Prado from the Trinidad Museum.

PEDRO BERRUGUETE, 1450?-1504.

THE ADORATION OF THE KINGS (No. 125). Canvas in gouache (serge). 3.50 × × 2.06 m. To the Prado from the Trinidad Museum.

For a long time it was attributed to Francisco de Cossa, the painter of the Quattrocento from Ferrara. The catalogue classifies this and the following painting as doors to an organ or an altar. In either case, it is a magnificent work of monumental size. It shows splendid Gothic-Renaissance architecture drawn with a firm hand in beautiful technique of mat colours.

PEDRO BERRUGUETE, 1450?-1504.

TWO KINGS. The right part of the composition of the painting *(Nos. 123-126).* Canvas in gouache (serge). To the Prado from the Trinidad Museum. In Spanish painting Berruguete represents the great conjunction of the old Flemish-Spanish School with the florescence of Italian Renaissance. In 1477 Berruguete was in Urbino in the service of Frederic of Montefeltro, whose study he painted together with Justus of Ghent. In his later production the influence of the paintings of Melozzo da Forli and Piero della Francesca is clear. The forms soften without losing their monumental character. There is increasing delicacy in the figures wrapped in light and shadow which gives them the special character of well finished form.

PEDRO BERRUGUETE, 1450?-1504.

ST. DOMINIC (No. 616). Wood 1.77 × 0.90 m. The painting originates from the Convent of St. Thomas in Avila. To the Prado from the Trinidad Museum. It may be the central panel of an altar-piece dedicated to the founder. The altar-piece would have been made up of nos. 609, 610, and 615. Both, this and the one of St. Thomas in the same convent, are late works of Berrugete's. The convent was finished en 1493. Brother Thomas of Torquemada had supervised its construction to the specifications of Hernán Núñez de Arnalta, the accountant for the Catholic Monarchs. When this painting was finished, Berruguete must have started the altar-piece for the cathedral in Avila. Upon his death in 1504 the altar-piece was still unfinished. Cruz Santos completed the work.

JUAN CORREA DE VIVAR.

Active between 1539 and 1552. Assessor in the cathedral in Toledo in 1532. Monk of the order of St. Jerome. The last reference to the artist is in 1561. Lit. Gómez Moreno, J. M., "Correa de Vivar". Archivo Español de Arte, no. 56 (1966), p. 299 ff.

THE DEATH OF THE VIRGIN (No. 671). Wood 2.54 × 1.47 m. The painting originates from the Transito Church of the Order of Calatrava in Toledo (until 1492 this was the synagogue of Samuel Levi).

The strong personality of John of Burgundy created an important center of painting to which Juan Correa de Vivar belonged a generation later. Notwithstanding a good knowledge of draftsmanship, Correa de Vivar fell into mannerisms and commonplaces that lacked animation and charm. Nevertheless, the figure of the donor, identified by Allende Salazar and Sánchez Cantón as Francisco de Rojas y Ayala of Calatrava, is very distinguished. It is a magnificent portrait executed with a fine sense of observation. Francisco de Rojas was the nephew of the similarly named ambassador of the Catholic Monarchs to Rome. Before his death in 1523 the ambassador commissioned Bramante to construct the shrine of St. Peter in Montorio.

JUAN CORREA DE VIVAR, 16thC.

NATIVITY (No. 690). Wood 2.28 × 1.83 m. The painting comes from Guisando. Together with nos. 687 and 689 it forms part of an altar-piece.

FERNANDO YAÑEZ DE LA ALMEDINA.

Probably born in La Almedina in Ciudad Real. He appears as a painter in Valencia in 1506. Between 1526 and 1531 or 1536 in Cuenca. Lit. Garín Ortiz de Taranco, Felipe Ma., *"Yáñez de la Almedina, pintor español".* Valencia, 1954.

ST. DAMIAN (No. 1339). Wood octagonal 0.95 × 0.73 m. Acquired by the Museum Foundation with a grant from the state in April 1929.

In 1506 the two brother were commissioned to paint an altar-piece of St. Cosmas and St. Damian for the chapel of the same name in the cathedral of Valencia. Later the chapel was dedicated to St. Catherine and the oldo altar-piece was removed. In 1936 the altar-piece burned in the Diocesan Museum. This painting may be another altar-piece dedicated to the medical saints.

FERNANDO YAÑEZ DE LA ALMEDINA.

ST. ANN, THE VIRGIN, ST. ELIZABETH, ST. JOHN, AND THE JESUS CHILD (No. 2805). Wood 1.40 × 1.19 m. Acquired from the parish of Infantes in Ciudad Real in 1941 with funds from the bequest of the count of Cartagena.

The work is an echo of Leonardo's famous painting in the Louvre done between 1507 and 1513. It is a work of the iconographical type *Anna Selbdrit,* to use the German phrase coined in art history for this production (Italian: "Anna Metterza").

FERNANDO YAÑEZ DE LA ALMEDINA.

ST. CATHERINE (No. 2902). Wood 2.12 × 1.12 m. Acquired from the heirs of the marquis of Casa Argudín by the Ministry of National Education in 1946.

It is considered by many to be the foresmost work in Spanish painting in the first half of the 16thC. If it is true that the "Fernando Spagnolo" who worked with Leonardo in Florence in 1505 on the now lost drawings of the battle of Anghiari is in fact Fernando Yáñez, then we must admit that Leonardo's teaching was perfectly assimilated. Impeccable technique, perfect knowledge of sketching, delicacy in the chiaroscuro, and harmony in the colours, even Leonardo's *morvidezza* accompany the delicate and elegant figure of the meditative saint.

JUAN VICENTE MASIP.

Born about 1475 in the Valencia region. Worked for the cathedral after 1522-25. Died before October 1550.

THE MARTYRDOM OF ST. YNEZ (No. 843). Wood 0.58 m. in diameter (tondo). Bought in 1826 by Ferdinand VII from the heirs of the marquis of Jura Real.

The echo that Yáñez and Llanos left in Valencia was profound and lasting as a generation of painters shows. The leader among them was Vicente Masip, the head of a family who were to make a fortune.

PEDRO MACHUCA.

Born in Toledo at the end of the 15thC, Machuca was a painter and architect. He spent time in Italy, constructor of the Palace of Charles V in Granada. He died in that city in 1550.

THE VIRGIN AND THE SOULS OF PURGATORY (No. 2579). Wood 1.67 × 1.35 m. Signed on the back where it says "Toledano". Bought in Italy in 1935 with state funds.

Machuca's stay in Italy as a soldier still left him time to appreciate the great lesson of the Renaissance. With no attempt to copy the memory of Raphael, the supremely complete balance between form and colour is obvious in this work. Attention to movement and the preoccupation with light foretell an incipient mannerism. The ample robes and the very body of the Virgin forebode it. It carries the date 1517.

PEDRO MACHUCA, end of the 15thC to 1550.

DESCENT FROM THE CROSS (No. 3117). Wood 1.41 × 1.28 m. Acquired by the Museum Foundation in London in 1961 from P. and D. Colnaghi.

At the edge of the painting one reads: "Doña Inés de Castillo, wife of García Rodríguez of Montalbo, governor of this town, ordered this altar-piece. It was finished in the year 1547". We don't know the locality that is referred to. Gómez Moreno dates the panel to the painter's Italian epoch. It is a magnificent example of the 16thC and shows the influence that the superior Roman Renaissance paintings must have exerted on Machuca's sharp eyes. The impeccable military figure in armour and the children are new in the iconography of this subject. The figure of Machuca as a painter is enriched by the two examples in the Prado. As an architect he will always be linked with the Palace of Charles V in Granada, which is the finest example of Renaissance architecture outside of Italy.

JUAN DE JUANES, 1523?-1579.

THE LAST SUPPER (No. 846). Wood 1.16 × 1.91. Acquired by Charles IV in 1801. Carried off by Joseph Bonaparte in 1814 to France. Returned to the Museum in 1818.

The painting shows echos of the famous Leonardo composition in the Dominican refectory of Santa Maria delle Grazie in Milan. Juanes may have known it from some engraving.

JUAN DE JUANES, 1523?-1579.

DON LUIS DE CASTELLA DE VILLANOVA, LORD OF BICORP (No. 855). Wood 1.05 × × 0.80 m. Probably acquired by Charles IV in Valencia, not in the Palace until 1814.

If the painting is really by Juan de Juanes, which is not at all certain, we must recognize that the Valencian wasted his talent as a portrait painter. The impeccable figure full of distinction and elegance is in the best tradition of Italian and Nordic Renaissance portraits. The technique, psychological penetration, dignity, and the exquisite and refined colour are qualities that place the portrait on a level with the great masters of the genre.

JUAN DE JUANES, 1523?-1579.

ECCE HOMO (No. 848). Wood 0.83 × 0.62 m. A present from the municipal council of Valencia to Charles IV. It came to the Prado from the palace in Aranjuez.

BLAS DEL PRADO.

Born in Toledo about 1545, strongly influenced by mannerism, died in the same city in 1592.

THE HOLY FAMILY, ST. ILDEFONSUS, ST. JOHN DE EVANGELIST, AND MASTER ALFONSO DE VELLEGAS (No. 1059). Canvas 2.09 × 1.65 m. In the palace in Madrid in 1818.

The suggestion and influence that Raphael's painting produced are obvious in this work by the Toledo Masters. Roman mannerism spread in Valencia, thus perpetuating the values of perfect balance and idealization between form and colour. But without the great masters who started mannerism, it was reduced to a formula. We must point out the excellent equilibrium of Alfonso de Villegas. It is in line with the Toledo realism of Cotan and Loarte and thus indicates a homogeneous trend in the Toledo tradition of painting.

NAVARRETE THE DUMB.

Born in Logroño about 1526. During a journey to Italy he worked with Titian in Venice (according to Father Sigüenza). Philip II appointed him court painter at the Escorial in 1568. He died in Toledo in 1579.

THE BAPTISM OF CHRIST (No. 1012). Wood 0.49 × 0.37 m. The painting is signed. Father Sigüenza mentions that it was in the prior's high cell. It came to the Academy of St. Ferdinand in 1827.

In order to understand Navarrete's work, one must visit the Escorial to see how his painting develops from prettily executed mannerism to the Venetian suggestions of colour and outline. Navarrete was decisively influenced by Venetian style both by his visit to Venice and Titian and by his contacts with the royal collections.

LUIS DE MORALES "THE DIVINE".

Born in Badajoz about 1500, died there in 1586. Lit. Gaya Nuño, A., *"Luis de Morales".* Madrid, 1961.

THE PRESENTATION OF THE CHILD JESUS (No. 943). Wood 1.46 × 1.14 m. Acquired by Charles IV. It comes from the New Palace.

The composition is repeated in the altar-piece of Arroyo de la Luz. It is not known with certainty where Morales spent his apprenticeship. One has suggested Seville because of its proximity to Badajoz. However, Toledo with its Renaissance painters may also have been where he started working. Ceán Bermúdez indicates Valladolid with Berruguete.

LUIS DE MORALES "THE DIVINE", about 1500-1586.

THE VIRGIN AND THE CHILD (No. 2656). Wood 0.84 × 0.64 m. Pablo Bosch Beques No. 24.

Of the several existing versions none surpasses this beautiful execution suffused with profound tenderness and religiosity.

ECCE HOMO (No. 2770). Size 0.40 × 0.28 m. Fernández-Durán Bequest.

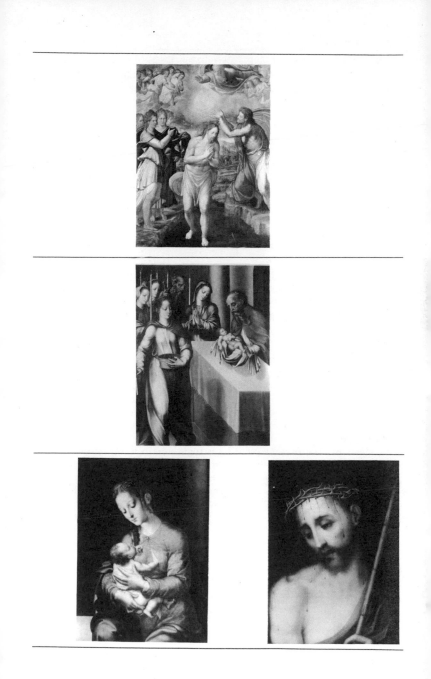

LUIS DE MORALES "THE DIVINE", about 1500-1586.

ST. JOHN OF RIVERA (No. 947). Wood 0.40 × 0.28 m. The painting was identified in 1945 by R. Robles and V. Castell. It was a besquest from doña María Enríquez de Valdés which was accepted by royal order on June 16, 1896.

ALONSO SANCHEZ COELLO.

Born in Benifayo (Valencia) in 1531/32. He travelled to Portugal and from there to Flanders where he completed his training under Moro. About 1554 back in Lisbon. After 1559 Philip II's court painter. He died in Madrid in 1588.

PHILIP II (No. 1036). Canvas 0.88 × 0.72 m. The painting was taken off to Paris by Bonaparte. It came to the Academy on the 30th of June, 1816, and was reclaimed by the Prado on June 7, 1827.

The great epoch of portraiture in Spanish painting begins with Sánchez Coello. His apprenticeship with Antonio Moro which was approved by Granvela in a letter to Philip II, shows that he was a pupil of the famous painter. From this educational experience stems his masterly and minute knowledge of Nordic technique. He combined this technique with a greater freedom in accessories in the tradition of Titian. The latter's influence becomes more obvious with the years as Sánchez Coello gets familiar with the royal collections. The present painting is registered in the inventory of the Alcázar in 1686, where it is attributed to Pantoja. It was Tormo who put in under Coello's name just as Sánchez Cantón did in his Catalogue from 1933. When we compare this painting to Pantoja's portrait of Philipe II in the Escorial, it is clear that it must have been painted before 1575. Diego Angulo thinks that it may be a work by Sofonisba Anguisciola.

ALONSO SANCHEZ COELLO, 1531/32-1588.

PRINCE CHARLES (No. 1136). Canvas 1.09 × 0.95 m. In 1936 the painting was in the Alcázar, in the Salon of the Furies, full length at that time.

It is a magnificent record of Philip II's firstborn. It shows a more moderate tone than the portrait of his father, the King, and is more closely related to Titian's style. It already expresses what will later become one of the great goals of Velazquez' portraits: bringing the personality of the portrait closer to the viewer. There has been much discussion about the age of the Prince and the date of the painting. It does not seem convincing that the Prince, who was in bad condition, ill, and poorly developed, can be more than fifteen years old. According to the 1637 inventory the portrait was full-length like the one in Vienna.

ALONSO SANCHEZ COELLO, 1531/32-1588.

PRINCESS ISABEL CLARA EUGENIA, 1579 (No. 1137). Canvas 1.16 × 1.02 m.

The Princess was approximately 13 years old. On April 18, 1599, she married her cousin, Archduke Albert of Austria. She died in Brussels in 1633. We are again surprised in this magnificent portrait by the graceful execution of the brush strokes and the vigourous captivation of the sweet and prudent princess, who governed Flanders with the tact and judgement characteristic of a great politician.

ALONSO SANCHEZ COELLO, 1531/32-1588.

THE PRINCESSES ISABEL CLARA EUGENIA AND CATALINA MICAELA (No. 1138). Canvas 1.35 × 1.49 m. In 1636 the painting was in the Alcázar; after that it was in the Retiro.

A replica with variations of this work, dated 1571, is in Buckingham Palace. Elías Tormo attributed an example in the Descalzas Reales Monastery in Madrid to Coello; it may have been painted in 1569-70. If the princesses were nine and ten years old, as Madrazo thinks, the painting would be from 1576.

DISCIPLES OF SANCHEZ COELLO, about 1580.

ISABEL CLARA EUGENIA AND MAGDALENA RUIZ (No. 861). Canvas 2.07 × 1.29 m. Described in the inventory of the Alcázar in 1600 and 1636, but without the name of the artist.

It is a painting of magnificent outline that must be placed among Coello's closest disciples. Madrazo attributed in without much evidence to Felipe de Liaño who died in 1625.

QUEEN ANNA OF AUSTRIA, FOURTH WIFE OF PHILIP II (No. 1284). Canvas 0.84 × × 0.67 m. The painting is of a poorer quality than the rest of Coello's work. It probably formed a pair together with the portrait of Philip II, No. 1036.

PANTOJA DE LA CRUZ.

Born in Valladolid in 1553. Disciple of Sanchez Coello's and Philip II's painter. Died in Madrid in 1608. Lit. Beruete, *"Pantoja de la Cruz"*, Madrid, 1924. Kusche, M., *"Pantoja de la Cruz"*, Madrid, 1964.

MARGARET OF AUSTRIA, WIFE OF PHILIP III, 1607 (No. 1032). Canvas 1.12 × 0.97 m.

Pantoja de la Cruz learned from Sánchez Coello to treat his portraits with dignity and truth. With him the impeccable court etiquete is introduced into Spanish painting.

EL GRECO, 1540-1614.

Born in Candia on Crete in 1540. Active in Venice before 1570, perhaps in Titian's circle. About 1570 in Rome, and from 1576 onward in Toledo, where he died in 1614. Lit. Cossio, M. Manuel, *"El Greco"*. Madrid, 1968; Mayer, A. L., *"El Greco"*. Munich, 1925 and 1931; Wethey, Harold E., *"El Greco"*. Princeton, 1962; Gudiol, José, *"El Greco"*. Barcelona, 1971; De Salas, Xavier, *"La obra pictórica completa de El Greco"*. Barcelona, 1977; Laissaine, Jacques, *"El Greco"*. Barcelona, 1973.

TRINITY, 1557 (No. 824). Wood 3.00 × 1.79 m. The painting originates from the altar-piece of St. Dominic the Elder in Toledo. It was acquired by Ferdinand VII in 1827 from the sculptor Valeriano Salvatierra.

This painting together with the Ascension in the Chicago Art Institute is the earliest work of El Greco's in Toledo. The suggestion and echo of Michelangelo's work are palpable. The muscular and turned body of Christ is modeled with the sculpture of Michelangelo still in mind. Lit. Wethey (No. 2).

EL GRECO, 1540-1614.

THE ANNUNCIATION, 1577-1580, according to Cossio *(No. 827)*. Wood 0.26 × × 0.19 m. The painting was bought in 1868 by Royal orden from doña Concepción Parody.

This may possibly be among the earliest works by El Greco. It is still very Venetian and shows the profund influence of Titian's compositions. Wethey dates it to 1570-75. Lit. Wethey (No. 38).

EL GRECO, 1540-1614.

A GENTLEMAN, 1584-94, according to Cossio *(No. 806)*. Canvas 0.46 × 0.43 m. In the Alcázar in Madrid en 1686 and in 1700.

It shows a superb head done with prodigious economy of means, full of expression, interior life, and subtle melancholy. Lit. Wethey (No. 139).

EL GRECO, 1540-1614.

GENTLEMAN WITH HIS HAND ON HIS CHEST, 1577-1584, according to Cossio *(No. 809)*. Canvas 0.81 × 0.66 m. In 1794 in La Quinta del Arco.

One of the most famous portraits by El Greco. D'Ors called it an "ethnic document", it is without doubt a fine example of the Cretan's painting. The intensification of the model for the sake of giving us the whole personality is a quality for wich El Greco had a perfect gift. Velázquez had one of these portraits in his atelier. The gentleman with his air of withdrawn spirituality and melancholic abstraction is the great lesson that the intellectuals of those days offer us in this exquisite painting. Wethey believes that it is from El Greco's first period, between 1577 and 1580. One has attempted to see it as portraying Santiago Juan de Silva, marquis of Montemayor and notary of Toledo. Lit. Wethey (No. 145).

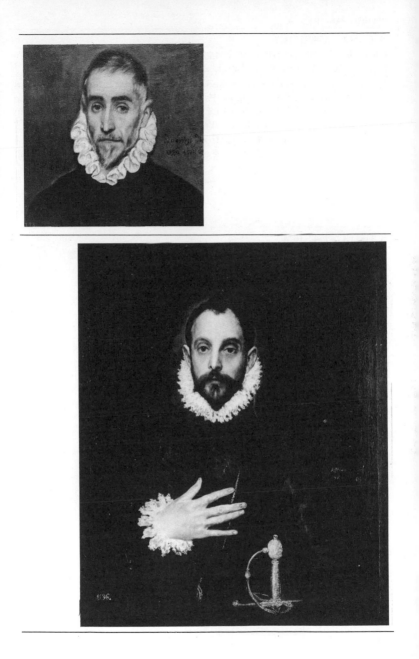

EL GRECO, 1540-1614.

THE CORONATION OF THE VIRGIN, 1590-95, according to Wethey *(No. 2645).* Canvas 0.90 × 1.00 m. Pablo Bosch Bequest No. 13.

This is a theme that El Greco repeated many times. Upon his death one of the inventories showed five examples. Paintings like the present are, with some variations, found in Toledo, San José, the hospital in Illescas, in the Epstein collection, and in Talaveruela. Lit. Wethey (No. 72).

ST. JOHN THE EVANGELIST, 1594-1604, according to Cossio *(No. 2444).* Canvas 0.90 × 0.77 m. Donated by Doctor César Cavanas in 1921. Lit. Wethey (No. 253).

EL GRECO, 1540-1614.

ST. ANDREW AND ST. FRANCIS, 1590-95, according to Wethey *(No. 2819).* Canvas 1.67 × 1.13 m. Acquired in January 1942 from the community of the Royal Monasterio of the Incarnation in Madrid.

Wethey calls it "the fines version of a pair of saints". The rich colouring and the caracterization of the two personages along with the magnificent execution of the brush strokes and the successful composition make this canvas one of the most fortunate acquisitions the Museum has ever made. It is in a perfect state of preservation. Until after the Spanish Civil War it was completely unknown. The canvas was donated to the Royal Monastery on October 3, 1676, by Mother Ana Augustina del Niño Jesús, daughter of the duke of Abrantes. Lit. Wethey (No. 197).

EL GRECO, 1540-1614.

THE CRUCIFIXION, 1584-94, according to Cossio *(No. 823).* Canvas 3.12 × 1.69 m. We do not know exactly where this painting comes from. Possibly from the house of the Jesuits of St. John the Baptist in Toledo, confiscated there by the Committee for the Expropriation of church property in 1836.

This is an extraordinary canvas from El Greco's last period of hallucinated and delirious composition and intonation. The keys to understanding El Greco's sorrowful versions of religious works is the pathetic attitude, the solem seriosusness of the Counterreformation, and the ascetic conception by the Loyola movement of the spiritual exercises. El Greco was the contemporary of St. Theresa and St. John of the Cross. Lit. Wethey (No. 75).

THE BAPTISM OF CHRIST, 1596 *(No. 821).* Canvas 3.50 × 1.44 m. Contracted by the Council of Castille on December 20, 1596. On July 12, 1600, the transfer of the altar-piece to Madrid was arranged.

One of the major works of El Greco's along with the Annunciation, on deposit in the Villanueva and Geltru Museum, and The Adoration of the Shepherds in Bucharest. The painting was commissioned for the Augustine convent in Madrid founded by Maria of Aragon, lady-in-waiting to Philip II's last wife. The religious themes of El Greco's last period now show an exacerbated fever that transforms them to vapor and music. Lit. Wethey (No. 14).

EL GRECO, 1540-1614.

THE HOLY FAMILY, 1594-1604, according to Cossio *(No. 826).* Canvas 1.07 × × 0.69 m. From a closed-down convent, but we do not know which.

This theme was also repeated by El Greco several times. There are four variants in existente. The composition of the painting in the Prado follows with variations the Holy Family painted for the Hospital of St. Anne, today in the Museum of the Holy Cross in Toledo. Lit. Wethey (No. 87).

EL GRECO, 1540-1614.

THE DOCTOR (Doctor Rodrigo de la Fuente?), 1577 and 1584, according to Cossio *(No. 807)*. Canvas 0.93 × 0.82 m. In 1686 in the Cierzo Gallery in the Alcázar in Madrid; in 1734 it came to the Retiro. Sánchez Cantón and Allende-Salazar have identified the person by comparison with a painting in the National Library as doctor Rodrigo de la Fuente, a famous Toledo doctor who was mentioned by Cervantes in "La ilustre fregona". He died in the city on the Tagus in 1589. Lit. Wethey (No. 149).

EL GRECO, 1540-1614.

A GENTLEMAN, about 1604-1614, according to Cossio *(No. 810)*. Canvas 0.64 × × 0.51 m.

The large ruff shows the baroque fashion at Philip III's court. In 1794 this painting was in the duke of Arco's villa. Lit. Wethey (No. 143).

YOUNG GENTLEMAN, about 1604-1614, according to Cossio *(No. 811)*. Canvas 0.55 × 0.49 m. In the last period of El Greco's portrait painting we notice a loss of the severity in the solemn pose of his early clients, who belonged to the court of Philip II. In 1794 the painting was in the duke of Arco's villa. Lit. Wethey (No. 144).

EL GRECO, 1540-1614.

A GENTLEMAN, about 1584 and 1594, according to Cossio *(No. 813)*. Canvas 0.65 × 0.55 m. In 1794 in the duke of Arco's villa. Lit. Wethey (No. 142).

THE LAWYER JERONIMO DE CEVALLOS, about 1604-1614, according to Cossio, perhaps in 1608 *(No. 812)*. Canvas 0.64×0.54 m. In 1704 in the duke of Arco's villa. The identification of this person is authenticated by an engraving by Pedro Angel, dated in 1613. Cevallos was a lawyer, alderman of Toledo, and author of legal and political works. He was 51 years old when he was painted. Lit. Wethey (No. 133).

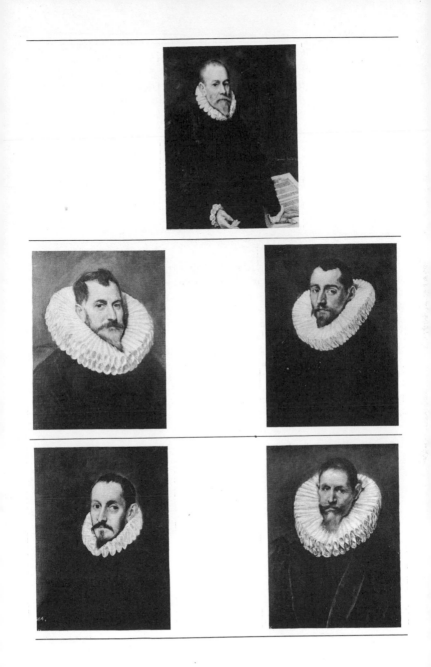

EL GRECO, 1540-1614.

ST. PAUL, about 1610-14 *(No. 2892).* Canvas 0.72 × 0.55 m.

Acquired in 1946 by the Ministry of National Education. Comes from the church of Almadrones in Guadalajara. Lit. Wethey (No. 192).

EL GRECO, 1540-1614.

THE ADORATION OF THE SHEPHERDS, about 1612-1614, according to Wethey *(No. 2988).* Canvas 3.19 × 1.80 m. Acquired by the sale in 1954.·

This extraordinary canvas from El Greco's last period was painted for his funeral chapel in the church of St. Dominic the Elder. In 1618 El Greco's mortal remains were transferred to another burial place in Santorcaz, but the painting and the altar-piece remained in St. Dominic's. When the painting of the Trinity was sold, this canvas took its place in the central altar-piece. The paroxysm, the weightlessness, and the struggle to achieve freedom from forms in mystic ecstasy reach their culmination in this work of genius. Here the figures shine like redhot coals in a mystic fire that is completely dreamlike. Lit. Wethey (No. 28).

SPANISH PAINTING UNDER THE HAPSBURGS

P. LOPEZ DE OSABA

The Renaissance movement as a European, and particulary Italian, phenomenon did not succeed in permeating Spain. That does not mean that there
were no examples of Renaissance aspirations, particulary in literature, but for
reasons that cannot be delved into here, the Renaissance did not manage to
cut a wide path in Spain. Except for some examples in the Spanish Levant,
painting moved from Gothic to Realism, where Spain was to take a leading
position. With this position consolidated, Spanish painting then immediately
turned to the Baroque.

In the Trecento and Quattrocento there is a development of idealization of
natural forms, of perspectives, of the rules of proportion, and of the
idolization of the human body that gropes towards and predicts the peak that
is reached at the end of the 15thC and the beginning of the 16thC. This
progression is never seen in Spanish painting of the same period. The main
vehicle for Renaissance painting to develop its three-dimensional character is
drawing, a talent which Spaniards are, frankly, not endowed with. With the
exception of Ribera, it is rare to see a Spanish painter with a large and
consistent production in this discipline. The genius Velázquez himself, did not
practice drawing, maybe because of his supreme domination and his habit
of doing things directly, "a la prima", characteristic of his expertise and
mastery. The Spanish painter chooses the "visual" impression more often than
the limited outline. In the case of engraving we have to wait practically until
Goya as late as the end of the 18thC and the beginning of the 19thC before
Spain reaches a high level in this genre.

The humanist process of idealization of man and of the return to pagan
antiquity as the supreme canon culminates marvellously in the work of
Raphael, of is a wonderful balance that is difficult to extend for long. The
Reformation with its dramatic effect on Europe put an end to this development. Michelangelo's profound religiosity already percieves that end, and his
successors, who lack the genius of the master, attempt to continue it without
great success. It is no wonder that a country as deeply religious and
conservative as Spain did not yield to the pagan insinuations of the
Renaissance. Spanish painting has to *bruler les etapes*. It does not show its
strength in sketching. The modeling of figures to the point where they appear

as architecture, almost three-dimensional (Tuscany and Rome), is not mastered in Spanish painting. The great Spanish gift of the painting of all periods is to see things "now" and "in the moment". It is to reduce things to their simplest form and almost to reify them. Spanish painting tends towards a reality wrapped in "its own light" —as Leonardo showed—. It leaves things vibrating in an eternal moment like a mirage or in a display of premature impressionism. This explains the preference that Spanish masters have for Venetian painting. With its free style and vibran colours that School is so different that Michelangelo lamented the lack of shape in the sketching when he saw one of the versions of Danae by Titian. But Michelangelo was not able to understand this lack of form. He was a Palestrina, Titian a Monteverdi. Better endowed for the pictorial than for the linear, to use Wölfflin's terminology. The Spaniards, therefore, felt extraordinarily attracted to the Venetians, who were so superbly represented in the royal collections. After the transitional school in Toledo with the figures of Sánchez Cotán (1561-1627), Tristán (1624), and Orrente (1588-1649), who had a strong influence on the painting at Court, and after the mastery of Ribera (1591-1627), who even at a distance exerted a strong influence, the arrival of Velázquez (1599-1660) marks the culmination of Spanish painting.

Like Velázquez, Zurbarán (1598-1664) brings this realism to the simplest things: his paintings and his people are always attempts at reification. His figures are scaffolds and skeletons that have been dressed up; they are always "still-lives". What interests him are things, serges, dusky coarse cloths, rustlings stilks, brocades, velvets, terracotta and porcelain, coppers and tins, all in exquisite and subtle colour but always maintaining and dominated by the most rigourous soberness. Alonso Cano (1601-1667) and Murillo (1618-1682) complete the great generation.

The constellation of great painters at Court ends with Carreño (1614-1685) and Claudio Coello (1642-1693), and with them ends the reign of the Hapsburgs. Nobody has painted as well as Carreño the dreadful sensation of decadence in a dynasty that has lost political power and biological strength as a result of so much "reckless consaguinity".

With Carreño and Claudio Coello we also reach the peak of the Baroque in Madrid. On the one hand it remains faithful to the recent lesson of Velázquez, but on the other hand it cannot escape from the temptation of colour presented by the Nordic painters, particulary of Rubens. The rigid Hapsburg etiquete marked the boundaries of painting in two great watersheds: the portraits of members of the royal family and the nobility that were to hang in their palaces, and the religious paintings for altars to decorate the churches and convents that the Court itself founded.

The popular and bourgeois element which was a characteristic theme for the art of the Reformation and its aversion for religious painting is a phenomenon that remains at the fringe of the Spanish court.

BIBLIOGRAPHY

Angulo Iñiguez, D.: *"Pintura del s. XVI"*, Ars Hispaniae. Madrid, 1954.

Angulo Iñiguez, D.: *"Pintura del s. XVII"*, tomo XV, Ars Hispaniae. Madrid, 1954.

Angulo Iñiguez, D., and Pérez Sánchez, A. E.: *"Pintura madrileña, primer tercio del s. XVII"*. Madrid, 1969.

Angulo Iñiguez, D., and Pérez Sánchez, A. E.: *"Pintura toledana, primera mitad del s. XVIII"*. Madrid, 1972.

Guinard, P.: *"Les peintres espagnoles"*. París, 1967.

Lafuente Ferrari, E.: *"La pintura española del s. XVII"*. Barcelona, 1935. En la historia de Arte Labor.

Lassaigne, J.: *"La peintre espagnole"*. París, 1958.

FELIPE RAMIREZ.

A painter from the first third of the 17thC.

STILL-LIFE. Signed and dated 1628 *(No. 2802).* Canvas 0.71 × 0.92 m. Acquired in 1940 with funds from the bequest of the count of Cartagena.

We know of the existence of this painter from what Ceán says about this still-life. It follows the Toledo tradition of Sánchez Cotán. It is a magnificent example of the realism and concision that are very Spanish characteristics of this genre.

BROTHER JUAN BAUTISTA MAINO, 1578-1649.

Born in Pastrana in 1578. Dominican monk in the convent of St. Peter Martyr in Toledo and drawing master to Philip IV. He died in Madrid on April 1, 1649.

THE ADORATION OF THE MAGI (No. 886). Canvas 3.15 × 1.74 m. The painting originates from St. Peter Martyr in Toledo. It belongs to the "Four Church Festivals" that were painted for the dominican convent in Toledo. Maino lived there for many years before joining the Court, where he was Philip IV's drawing master. There is an effect of great movement in the canvas. The ivy, the ample clothes of the figures, and the delicate modeling of them all contribute to a quality of great plasticity. The magnificent example of still-life in the lower part of the painting is a very traditional motive in the Toledo School.

BROTHER JUAN BAUTISTA MAINO, 1578-1649.

THE ARRIBAL OF THE HOLY GHOST (No. 3018). Canvas 2.85 × 1.63 m. The painting belonged to the altar-piece of St. Peter Martyr in Toledo. In 1939 it came from the Archaeological Museum in Toledo to the Prado, where it was restored. Together with No. 886 it belongs to the "Four Church Festivals".

BROTHER JUAN BAUTISTA MAINO, 1578-1649.

THE RECAPTURE OF BAHIA IN BRAZIL (No. 885). Canvas 3.09 × 3.81 m. Painted for the Great Hall of the Realm in the Palace of the Buen Retiro. It was returned from Paris in 1815. Until 1827 it was in the Academy and since then it has been in the Prado.

The victory was attained by Fabrique de Toledo. He is showing the soldiers the tapestry depicting Philip IV being crowned by the Duke of Olivares and by Victoria. The persons to the right of the general may be his lieutenant Juan de Orellana and the chief of the fleet, Juan Fajardo de Guevara. The left half of the canvas is painted with exquisitely delicate colours that are surprising for that period of Spanish painting.

BROTHER JUAN BAUTISTA MAINO, 1578-1649.

A GENTLEMAN (No. 2595). Canvas 0.96 × 0.73 m. Acquired in April of 1936 from Cristóbal Colón, with funds from the bequest of the count of Cartagena.

The evolution of Spanish portraiture from El Greco to Velázquez is well represented by this painting that brings together the two great figures. It is a half-length portrait of a gentleman who is serenely distinguished and impeccably painted.

FRANCISCO HERRERA, 1576-1656.

Born in Seville about 1576. Briefly, Velázquez' first teacher. He died in Madrid in 1656. Lit Thacher, *"The Paintings of Francisco Herrera; the Elder"*, The Art Bulletin, 1937; Cook, *"Francisco de Herrera"*, Boletín de la Asociación Española de Excursiones, 1907.

ST. BONAVENTURE TAKES THE VOWS OF ST. FRANCIS (No. 2441 A). Canvas 2.31 × 2.15 m. Given to the Museum in 1925 by Dr. Joaquín Carballo.

Painted along with three others by Herrera and four by Zurbarán for the church of the seminary of St. Bonaventure in Seville. The series of paintings was commissioned on December 30, 1627. A magnificent painting of great plastic quality. It makes Herrera come close to Zurbarán's good performances. The modeling of the faces, the treatment of the light, and the temperamental seriousness of the figures are a great advance in the painting of the period.

FRANCISCO RIBALTA, 1565-1628.

Born in Solsona in Lérida. Buried in Valencia on January 14, 1628. Lit. Fitz Darby, *"Francisco Ribalta"*, Cambridge, 1938; Espresati, C. C., *"Ribalta"*. Barcelona, 1948.

CHRIST EMBRACED BY ST. BERNARD (No. 2804). Canvas 1.58 × 1.13 m. Acquired in 1940 with funds from the bequest of the count of Cartagena. The plastic excellence of this group made it believed earlier that the painting was a work by Zurbarán. It is from Ribalta's last period and forms a part of the series made for the Carthusian monastery of Portacoeli, between 1627 and 1628.

FRANCISCO RIBALTA, 1565-1628.

ST. FRANCIS BEING CONSOLED BY AN ANGEL MUSICIAN (No. 1062). Canvas 2.04 × × 1.58 m. Bought in 1801-02 by Charles IV from the Capuchin monks of Valencia. In 1818 it was in Aranjuez.

A magnificent example of Baroque as it expresses Spanish spirituality of the 17thC. A similar theme is brought to the peak by Bernini in his St. Teresa. The love of small things: the oil lamp, the serge robe, and the still-lives, along with the warm colour of his paintings, made Ribalta a very Spanish painter.

JOSE RIBERA, 1591-1652.

Born in Játiva in 1591. In 1616 working in Naples. Sponsored by the dukes of Osuna and the Spanish viceroys of Naples. In 1626 member of the Academy of St. Luke. Caravaggio's paintings influenced his first period. He died in Naples on September 2, 1652. Lit. Mayer, A. L., *"Jusepe Ribera"*, Leipzig, 1923; Trapier, E. du Gué, *"Ribera"*, New York, 1952; Spinosa, N. and E. Pérez Sánchez, A., *"Ribera"*, Milán, 1970; Barcelona, 1979.

ARCHIMEDES, 1630 *(No. 1121).* Canvas 1.25 × 0.81 m. Came to the Museum from the monastery of the Escorial, where it was registered in 1764.

The influence of Caravaggio's tenebrism and of the best of contemporary Italian painting is clearly seen in this painting and in others by Ribera. These influences dominated him at least until 1635. But *El Spagnoletto* introduces the actual individual into his figures. His ragged persons have all the force of being impressively real. The painting is signed. Lit. Spinosa, E. Pérez Sánchez, No. 40, p. 99.

JOSE RIBERA, 1591-1652.

ST. ANDREW, 1632? *(No. 1078).* Canvas 1.23 × 0.95 m. Came from the Escorial in 1837.

The vigourous quality of the drawing, the spotlight coming almost straight down from above in a pure sense of contrast, these were the most important benefits the reform bestowed on religious art. This art had a strongly ascetic character and a profoundly mystical expression. Lit. Trapier (Illust. 60, p. 96), Spinosa, N. and E. Pérez Sánchez, No. 65, p. 102.

THE GREEK SCULPTOR GAMBAZO, 1632 *(No. 1112).* Canvas 1.25 × 0.98 m. Brought from the Escorial in 1837.

It has been said that it belongs to a series of "the Senses". This painting should then represent the sense of touch. Lit. Trapier (p. 77), Spinosa, N. and E. Pérez Sánchez, A., No. 65, p. 102.

JOSE RIBERA, 1591-1652.

THE MARTYRDOM OF ST. BARTHOLOMEW (No. 1101). Canvas 2.34 × 2.34 m. In 1666 in the Alcázar in Madrid.

The large canvas is like an immense stage. The theme is treated with the dignity of tragedy. It already shows a baroque design and even the opulence of colours. If it was painted in 1630, it would indicate that Ribera's tenebrist period gave way to a more luminous vision of themes as in the Venetian style. Lit. Trapier (illus. 41, 43, and 44, pp. 30, 65); Spinosa, N. and E. Pérez Sánchez, A., No. 152, p. 116.

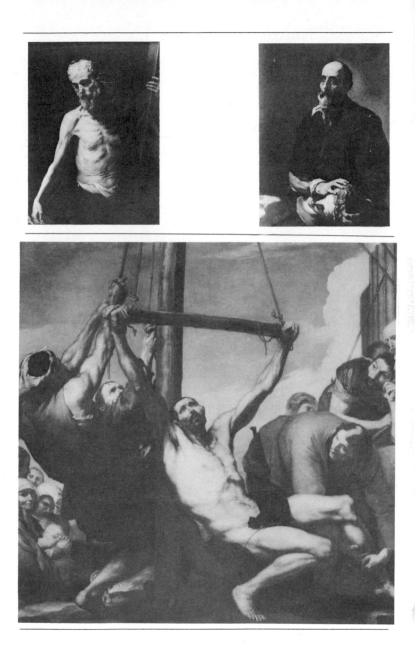

JOSE RIBERA, 1591-1652.

ISAAC AND JACOB, 1637 *(No. 1118).* Canvas 1.29 × 2.89 m. Recorded in the 1700 inventory of the Alcázar in Madrid. It narrates the passage from Genesis XXVII where Isaac "felt him and said, the voice is Jacob's voice, but the hands are the hands of Esau". The painting is clearly narrative, done in the Venetian style in sumptuous colours with a fluent subject-matter and high quality in drawing. About this time Ribera won the competition to paint the Pietà in the sacristy of the Carthusian monastery in San Merino, where he worked for the rest of his life. Lit. Trapier (illust. 91, 92, p. 143). Spinosa, N. and E. Pérez Sánchez, A., No. 111, p. 110.

JOSE RIBERA, 1591-1652.

ST. CHRISTOPHER, 1637 *(No. 1111).* Canvas 1.27 × 1.00 m. Salvaged in the fire in the Alcázar in 1734. In 1772 it was in the sacristy of the Palace. Lit. Trapier (illust. 87, pp. 136, 139). Spinosa, N. and E. Pérez Sánchez, A., No. 116, p. 111.

JOSE RIBERA, 1591-1652.

JACOB'S DREAM, 1639 *(No. 1117).* Canvas 1.79 × 2.33 m. In 1746 at La Granja. In 1827 from the Academy of St. Ferdinand. Mayer thinks it was painted in 1746 and Tormo in 39.

The gradual lightening of Ribera's palette speaks for this date. The fact that some works by Ribera were formerly classified under Veronese or Murillo indicates Ribera's course from very dark colours to Venetian clarity. Lit. Trapier (illust. 113, 114, pp. 165-66). Spinosa, N. and E. Pérez Sánchez, A., No. 150, p. 115.

FRANCISCO ZURBARAN, 1598-1664.

Born in Fuente de Cantos (Badajoz), in 1598. In 1614 in Seville. The municipal government of that city gave him the litle of "master of the City of Seville". In 1634 in Madrid where he died on August 27, 1664. Lit. Soria Martín, S., *"The paintings of Zurbarán"*, London, 1955. Gaya Nuño, A., *"Zurbarán"*, París, 1962. Caturla, M., *"Zurbarán"*, a study and catalogue of the exhibition held in Granada in June 1953.

THE VISION OF ST. PETER NOLASCO, 1629 *(No. 1236)*. Canvas 1.79 × 2.23 m. Given by dean López Cepero to Ferdinand VII in exchange for copy of the painting of Mariana de Austria by Velázquez.

The painting is one in a series consisting of 21 scenes from the life of the holy founder of the Order of our Lady of Ransom ("Mercedarians"). Zurbarán has been the last of the great Spanish master of the 17thC to reach the fame that he deserved. Not everything he painted reached the same height. Distances, movements of masses, and nudes were alien to his style of painting. He preferred concrete details, which is why his still-lives are unique. We might say that even in his most devout paintings there is this tendency to reification. While we admire El Greco, Ribera, and Velázquez for their deep psychology, we marvel at Zurbarán's figures for their tangible qualities: the lavish differentiation in the quality of the fabric of the clothes which really are hung on mannequins. Lit. Soria (30).

FRANCISCO ZURBARAN, 1598-1664.

APARITION OF THE APOSTLE PETER TO ST. PETER NOLASCO, 1629 *(No. 1237)*. Canvas 1.79 × 2.23 m. Companion piece to No. 1236. The rich quality of Zurbarán's whites has been pointed out many times and is abundantly clear in this painting. The economy and austerity of the painter together with the absence of Baroque ornamentation are the key to understanding his success among the clerics that were the principal patrons of the artist.

FRANCISCO ZURBARAN, 1598-1664.

STILL-LIFE, 1633? *(No. 2803)*. Canvas 0.46 × 0.84 m. A present to the Museum in 1940 from Francisco de A. Cambó. There is evidence to support the attribution of this painting to Zurbarán: comparison with signed works, analogues pieces of pottery and metal in other paintings, and the overall high quality of this still-life. It is precisely in this subject that the Extremadura painter reaches masterly heights. The qualities of the objects that interested him so much are treated in full detail: rough earthenware pots, glazed pottery, crockery, the qualities of the ceramics and metal vessels are truly the subject of the painting. Zurbarán glorifies the most humble implements and their perfect proportions and colour. Lit. Soria (73).

FRANCISCO ZURBARAN, 1598-1664.

ST. CASILDA, 1640 *(No. 1239)*. Canvas 1.84 × 0.90 m. In 1814 in the Palace in Madrid.

It is one of the best pieces by Zurbarán in the Prado. The dress of the saint follows 17thC fashion. Zurbarán uses the dress as a pretext to show off the lavish range of opulent colours and the rich textures of the fabrics. His great sobriety and elegance contrast with the pictorial abundance of his baroque contemporaries. His St. Casilda may be considered the standard for Spanish women of the 17 thC. Lit. Soria (181).

DIEGO SILVA VELAZQUEZ, 1599-1660.

Born in Sevilla. Baptized on June 6, 1599. After a short stay in Herrera's atelier, he moved on to Pacheco's in 1610. In 1622 first journey to Madrid, in 1623 his second and decisive one. That same year he was appointed Philip IV's court painter. Influenced by Italian tenebrism and more extensively by the Venetian School. In 1628-29 he met Rubens in Madrid. First journey to Italy in 1629-30, the second in 1649-51. In 1659 he was invested with the Order of Santiago in Madrid. He died on August 7, 1660. Lit. Justi, Carl, *"Velázquez und sein Jahrhundert"*, Bonn, 1888; Spanish version, Madrid, 1953; Mayer, A. L., *"Velázquez"*, London, 1936; C. V. Lafuente Ferrari, E., *"Velázquez"*, London-New York, 1943; Curtis, Charles B., *"Velázquez and Murillo"*, London, 1883; López-Rey, J., *"Velázquez"*, London, 1963: Gudiol, J., *"Velázquez"*, Barcelona, 1973.

THE VENERABLE MOTHER JERONIMA DE LA FUENTE, 1610 *(No. 2873)*. Canvas 1.60 × × 1.10 m. Came from the convent of Santa Isabel in Toledo. In 1944 is bought by the Ministry of Education and Science with the aid of the Museum Foundation.

It is the most vigourous paintings in the Prado from Velázquez's Seville period. We see in it the seeds of his great paintings: his grasp of the individuality of his models, and his respect for the nature of things. At the age of 65 Mother Jeronima set out to found convents in Manila. This painting became publicly known at the exposition in Madrid in 1926. Lit. Gudiol (No. 17), Mayer (No. 546).

VELAZQUEZ, 1599-1660.

DON FRANCISCO PACHECO (?), about 1619 *(No. 1209)*. Canvas 0.40 × 0.36 m. We owe the identification of Pacheco to J. Allende-Salazar. Pacheco was Velázquez' second teacher and his father-in-law. Lit. Gudiol (No. 31), Mayer (No. 390).

VELAZQUEZ, 1599-1660.

THE INFANTE DON CARLOS, about 1626-27 *(No. 1188).* Canvas 1.09 × 1.25 m. The painting was in the Palace and between 1816 and 1827 in the Academy of San Fernando, where it was mistaken for a portrait of Philip IV.

The Prince Don Carlos was the second son of Philip III. He was born on September 15, 1607, and died on July 30, 1632. He was fond of painting and poetry. The Prince's great naturalness and noble appearence —the class and lineage, as D'Ors would say— are manifest in this admirable canvas, an example of court painting. Lit. Gudiol (No. 44), Mayer (No. 294).

VELAZQUEZ, 1599-1660.

PHILIP III, about 1628 *(No. 1183).* Canvas 0.57 × 0.44 m. In 1744 in the duke of Arco's villa.

In the year 1629 Rubens came to Madrid. The Flemish painter's lavish colouring may have influenced the Sevillian. It may be that this portrait with its brilliant colours received such an influence. Today we know that it is a fragment of another, larger painting. Lit. Gudiol (No. 43), Mayer (No. 203).

VELAZQUEZ, 1599-1660.

THE DRUNKARDS OR THE TRIUMPH OF BACCHUS, about 1628-29 *(No. 1170).* Canvas 1.65 × 2.25 m. Listed in the inventory of the Palace from 1636.

In Rubens' mythological compositions are pleasing visions that overflow with joy, vitality, and colour. In Velázquez' painting there is a joyful group of rascals, shown with neither complaisance nor reprimand. He does not paint gods, but men from the tavern. Wine has lit up their eyes and lent them a happiness that borders on stupidity. X-rays show that the painting was retouched. Possibly it was damaged in the fire in the Alcázar. Justi pointed out that the canvas was larger and had been retouched. The background cannot pass for a Velázquez, either. Lit. Gudiol (No. 53), Mayer (No. 51).

VELAZQUEZ, 1599-1660.

CRUCIFIXION, about 1632 *(No. 1167).* Canvas 2.48 × 1.69 m. Comes from the convent of San Plácido in Madrid. In 1829 Ferdinand VII sent it to the Museum.

Without any of the rhetorical dramatism, so fashionable during the Baroque, Velázquez gives us this Christ, alone, serene, in an attitude of supreme dignity. The iconography approaches the norms prevailing in Seville in the 17thC, as described by Pacheco. Lit. Gudiol (No. 98); Mayer (No. 13).

VELAZQUEZ, 1599-1660.

THE LANCES OR THE SURRENDER OF BREDA, before April 28, 1635 *(No. 1172).* Canvas 3.07 × 3.67 m.

In 1590 Breda fell into Dutch hands. There followed a twelve years truce under Philip III. In 1621 Philip IV ascended to the throne and started the war anew. A Genovese aristocrat, the marquis of Spinola, who was in the service of Philip IV, received a laconic order from the King that expressed the latter's wish clearly: "Marquis. Take Breda. I, the King." Europe watched Breda as a model of military tactics. The operation were observed by famous benerals who had come to witness the strategy. Princess Isabel Clara, the King's aunt, sent for the engraver Callot to make rough sketches of the site. Inside the fortified city the chief of operations was Justinus of Nassau, a bastard of the House of Orange. Spinola had with him the marquis of Leganés and Carlos Coloma and 30.000 men besides. On July 2, 1625, after a heroic defense, Justinus surrendered. Spinola travelled for the last time from Barcelona to Genoa when Velázquez made his first journey to Italy. The painting is counted among the most glorious contributions that a person has ever left to the history of art. The theme is an "Academy of Honour" and the representation of military etiquete and courtesy. It shows a ceremony elevated to the category of a work of art. Velázquez was not present at the siege, but he may well have known Callot's works. The blue backgrounds, the columns of smoke, and the flooded areas all fade away in the background of the painting, all touched by the same breeze, while the foreground shows two great groups of gentlemen —conquerors and conquered— who with incredible realism frame the two main figures. Lit. Gudiol (No. 76), Mayer (No. 78).

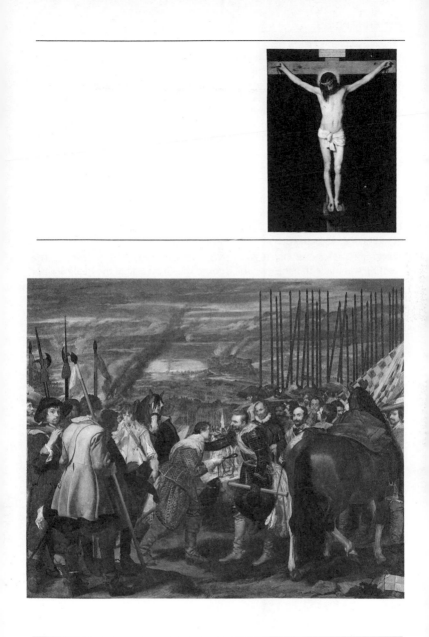

VELAZQUEZ, 1599-1660.

PHILIP IV ON HORSEBACK, about 1636 *(No. 1178).* Canvas 3.01 × 3.14 m. Painted for the Great Hall of the Realms.

A masterly representation of the Monarch in profile. Velázquez continues to perfect his representation of landscapes (in this case El Prado) by his use of silver-gray and blue backgrounds with which the Sevillian succeeds in creating an extraordinary climate of space. The retouches demonstrate once more the control and esthetic demand the painter made on himself. Lit. Gudiol (No. 78), Mayer (No. 185).

VELAZQUEZ, 1599-1660.

PRINCE BALTASAR CARLOS, 1635-36 *(No. 1180).* Canvas 2.09 × 1.73 m. The painting was made to hang ever the door to the Great Hall of the Realms. Later in the Palace.

Prince Baltasar Carlos was born on October 17, 1629, and died in Zaragoza on October 9, 1646. In this painting Velázquez reaches an extraordinary brilliance and fluency. The background is clean and transparent, the young prince exhibits liveliness, naturalness, and freshness. The deformation of the horse was intended to compensate for the angle at which the painting was to be seen in its position ever the door of the Great Hall of the Realms. Lit. Gudiol (No. 77), Mayer (No. 261).

VELAZQUEZ, 1599-1660.

DON GASPAR DE GUZMAN, COUNT OF OLIVARES, 1634-36 *(No. 1186).* Canvas 3.13 × 2.39 m. In the Palace from 1772 onwards.

An exalted and opulent, almost flattering representation of Philip IV's minister. If the portrait of the King shines with elegance and distinction, this one demostrates a culmination of the minister's empty vanity with full unfurling of Baroque imagination. Guzmán was born in the Spanish embassy in Rome, where his father was the ambassador, on January 6, 1587. He was Philip IV's primer minister until January 17, 1643. He died in Toro on July 22, 1645. Charles III acquired the painting in 1769. Lit. Gudiol (No. 73), Mayer (No. 309).

VELAZQUEZ, 1599-1660.

VIEW OF THE GARDEN OF THE VILLA MEDICI IN ROME, 1650-51 *(No. 1210).* Canvas 0.48 × 0.42 m. The painting is listed in the 1666 inventory of the Alcázar. Lit. Gudiol (No. 62), Mayer (No. 154).

In 1649, one year after the treaty of Westphalia, Velázquez went to Italy for the second time, commissioned by the King to buy works of art. These two small canvases are from that period. Both the present painting and No. 1210 foreshadow marvellously what painting would become. Velázquez shows himself here as the first impressionist in the exquisite moment of light in the impression of open air, in the lightness of the brush, and in the sketchings. On the other hand, in these sketches in which the program required by portrait painting does no exist, Velázquez gives himself over to his most secret taste: unencumbered nature shining with light and colour. Lit. Gudiol (No. 61), Mayer (No. 154).

VELAZQUEZ, 1599-1660.

VIEW OF THE GARDEN OF THE VILLA MEDICI IN ROME, 1650-51. *(No. 1211).* Canvas 0.44 × 0.38 m.

VELAZQUEZ, 1599-1660.

THE MENINAS OR THE FAMILY OF PHILIP IV (No. 1174). Canvas 3.18 × 2.76 m. In 1666 the painting was in the Summer Room in the Alcázar in Madrid.

In 1843, in Pedro de Madrazo's catalogue, it is called Las Meninas (The Ladies-in-Waiting) for the first time. It is the major work of Velázquez' production and one of the greatest attainments in the history of painting universally. In this painting Velázquez gives a masterly example of "time" and "light". Time, because it depicts an eternal instant. Light, atmosphere, because space envelops the persons, the shadows, the half-lights, and the light shining directly on the princess, who reigns here in a splendid way. It is a reflection of reality, or rather, the clear glass over a moment of reality, captured for eternity. The size of the painting and this feeling of the naturalness of proportions and space make the visitor feel integrated into the scene. Hence the remark that is attributed to Theophile Gautier after he had looked at the canvas for a long time. The subordination of the whole to a unity of light and the concentration of interest in a central point within the great areal perspective are, as Ortega has said, the Copernican revolution in painting. From left to right: Velázquez, María Agustina Sarmiento, "lady-inwaiting", daughter of Diego Sarmiento de Sotomayor, marquis of Salvatierra; princess Margarita, who in time was to marry the emperor Leopoldo, on December 12, 1666; Isabel de Velasco, also "lady-in-waiting", daughter of the count of Colmenares; Maribarbola, a German by birth; Nicolás Portosanto or Pertusato; behind, María de Ulloa; next to her an escorting officer; leaving the room through the door in the background, José Nieto Velázquez, the Queen's chief of tapestry; reflected in the mirror, Philip IV and Queen Mariana de Austria. Lit. Gudiol (No. 155), Mayer (No. 166).

VELAZQUEZ, 1599-1660.

QUEEN MARIANA DE AUSTRIA, 1652-53 *(No. 1191).* Canvas 2.31 × 1.31 m. In 1700 recorded in the Escorial, whence it came to the Museum in 1841.

Queen Mariana was the daughter of Maria of Austria and emperor Ferdinand III, and thus the niece of King Philip IV. She was supposed to have married Prince Baltasar Carlos, but when he died in 1646, the man who was her uncle and would have been her father-in-law took her as his wife. The result of this atrocious consanguinity was Charles II. When the princess arrived in Madrid, she was fifteen years old. The present painting is among the finest female representations by Velázquez in the Prado. There are replicas of the portrait in France and Vienna that do not have curtains. For that reason the curtains, in this painting may have been added later. Lit. Gudiol (No. 147), Mayer (No. 484).

VELAZQUEZ, 1599-1660.

THE SPINNERS OR THE FABLE OF ARACHNE, about 1651 *(No. 1173).* Canvas 2.20 × 2.89 m. The painting belonged to Don Pedro de Arce, the King's hunter. That explains its late incorporation into the royal collections, where it is not documented until the 18thC. It was in the Buen Retiro and in the new Palace.

The subject is the fable of Arachne that Ovid tells of in the Metamorphoses. As in the small paintings from the Villa Medici, Velázquez is not concerned with portrayals here. His vision is freer, more independent and masterful than in other works. The mythological theme is treated and reduced to a pure reality that is pure visuality, as Ortega noted. As in Las Meninas, it is the atmosphere that plays the main role. There the background was dark; here it is the contrary. Additional strips have been added to the painting on all four sides, perhaps as a result of damages that it suffered in the fire in the Alcázar. Lit. Gudiol (No. 133), Mayer (No. 130).

JUAN BAUTISTA DEL MAZO.

Mazo may have been born in the bishopric of Cuenca, probably in Beteta. Velázquez' assistant son-in-law. Died in Madrid on February 10, 1667.

PRINCIPE BALTASAR CARLOS, 1645 *(No. 1221).* Canvas 2.09 × 1.44 m. In the Retiro and from 1816 to 1827 in the Academy of San Fernando.

For a long time it was thought to be a work by Velázquez. Beruete the Elder considered it one of Mazo's best paintings.

J. B. DEL MAZO, died 1667.

EMPRESS MARGARITA OF AUSTRIA, about 1666 *(No. 888).* Canvas 2.09 × 1.47 m. In 1695 in the Alcázar in Madrid.

The daughter of Philip IV and queen Mariana, Margarita, was born on July 12, 1651. She married emperor Leopold on December 12, 1666 and died on March 12, 1673. She is the infanta who is portrayed in Velázquez' painting Las Meninas. The presence of Velázquez and Mazo's long years of close association with him influenced Mazo's work. We see that influence in the severe nobleness of this painting where Mazo proves to be great painter.

ALONSO CANO.

Born in Granada on March 19, 1601. He died in the same city on September 3, 1667. Lit. Martínez Chumillas, M., *"Alonso Cano",* Madrid, 1949; Mayer, A. L., *"El racionero Alonso Cano y el arte de Granada",* Jahrbuch der preussischen Kunstsammlungen, XXX and XXXI; Wethey, H., *"Alonso Cano, Painter, Sculptor, Architect",* Princeton, 1955.

THE MIRACLE OF THE WELL, 1638-40 (No. 2806). Canvas 2.16 × 1.49 m. Came to the Museum in 1941 from the convent of Las Bernardas.

Palomino praised it in his day. Cano's violent and difficult temper was not translated into his work, which shows exquisite colouration and perfect mastery of sketching.

ALONSO CANO, 1601-1667.

THE VIRGIN WITH THE CHILD. 1646-50 *(No. 627).* Canvas 1.62 × 1.07 m. Acquired by Charles IV.

This Virgin and Child show neither the secluded and mystic passion of Zurbarán, nor the controlled sobriety of Velázquez but rather Cano's feminine ideal. A very similar painting. No. 630, is today on deposit in the Museum of Granada. Lit. Wethey (illust. 75, p. 162).

ALONSO CANO, 1601-1667.

THE DEAD CHRIST SUPPORTED BY AN ANGEL, 1646-52 *(No. 2637).* Canvas 1.37 × × 1.00 m. No. 5 in the Pablo Bosch bequest. It is signed.

The theme is repeated with variations (No. 629). In the present version the body, not without beauty, reminds us of the ample form of Flemish painters. Lit. Wethey (illust. 80, p. 151).

THE DEAD CHRIST SUPPORTED BY AN ANGEL, 1646-52 *(No. 629).* Canvas 1.78 × × 1.21 m. Acquired from the marquis of La Ensenada in 1769. (Workshop?) Lit. Wethey (illust. 81, p. 151).

ALONSO CANO, 1601-1667.

ST. BENEDICT DURING THE VISION OF THE GLOBE, AND THE THREE ANGELS, 1657-60 *(No. 625).* Canvas 1.66 × 1.23 m. In 1700 in the workshop of the court painters in the Alcázar in Madrid. Lit. Wethey (p. 166).

BARTOLOME ESTEBAN MURILLO.

Baptized in Sevilla on January 1, 1618. Died in the same city on April 3, 1682. Lit. Mayer, A. L., *"Murillo"*, Leipzig, 1904; Montoto, S., *"Murillo"*, Seville, 1923, Barcelona, 1932; Gaya Nuño, L. A., *"Murillo"*, Milán, 1972; Barcelona, 1978.

THE HOLY FAMILY WITH THE LITTLE BIRD, about 1650 *(No. 960)*. Canvas 1.44 × × 1.88 m. Appears for the first time in La Granja in 1746 where it belonged to Isabel de Farnesio's collection. It was carried off to Paris by Joseph I whence it was returned in 1818.

Murillo is the minstrel of popular religiosity. It was the Church that on a grand scale commissioned paintings from Murillo as it did from almost all the painters of the 17thC with the exception of Velázquez. Within this limitation there is a clear tendency to depict religious life and pleasant spirituality that gave Murillo popular support. Lit. Gaya Nuño (No. 27, p. 88).

MURILLO, 1618-1682.

THE ANNUNCIATION (No. 969). Canvas 1.83 × 2.25 m. May be considered from Murillo's first period. In 1772 in the Palace. Lit. Gaya Nuño (No. 59, p. 91).

MURILLO, 1618-1682.

THE VISION OF ST. FRANCIS IN THE PORZIUNCOLA CHAPEL, 1667 (No. 981). Canvas 2.06 × 1.46 m. Acquired by Charles IV. In 1814 in the Palace in Madrid.

The theme was painted by Murillo several times. Lit. Gaya Nuño (No. 186, p. 103).

THE GOOD SHEPHERD (No. 962). Canvas 1.23 × 1.01 m. Belonged to Isabel de Farnesio's collection. In 1794 in Aranjuez. Lit. Gaya Nuño (No. 108, p. 96).

MURILLO, 1618-1682.

THE FOUNDATION OF SANTA MARIA LA MAGGIORE IN ROME: I, THE PATRICIAN JOHN'S DREAM (No. 994). Canvas 2.32 × 5.22 m. semicircle. The two paintings came to the Museum in 1901 from the Academy of San Fernando. They had arrived there from France in 1816.

This semicircle like No. 995, was painted for the church of Santa María la Banca in Seville. It was commissioned from Murillo by Justino Neve, a Sevillian canon and friend of the painter's, who founded the Hospital de Venerables Sacerdotes. The church was inaugurated in 1665. Marshal Soult seized the paintings and gave them to the Napoleon Museum. In Paris, under the direction of the architect Bercier, the spandrels were added. Nicolás Minuissir, and adjutant to general Miguel de Alava, requisitioned the paintings in 1815. By their sketchy, ethereal aspect, by the qualities of their beautiful colour, and by their elegant and natural composition, they may be considered major works in the production of the Sevillian painter. Lit. Gaya Nuño (No. 103, p. 95).

THE FOUNDATION OF SANTA MARIA LA MAGGIORE IN ROME: II, THE PATRICIAN REVEALS HIS DREAM TO THE POPE (No. 995). Canvas 2.32 × 5.22 m. The painting came to the Museum in 1901. Lit. Gaya Nuño (No. 104, p. 95).

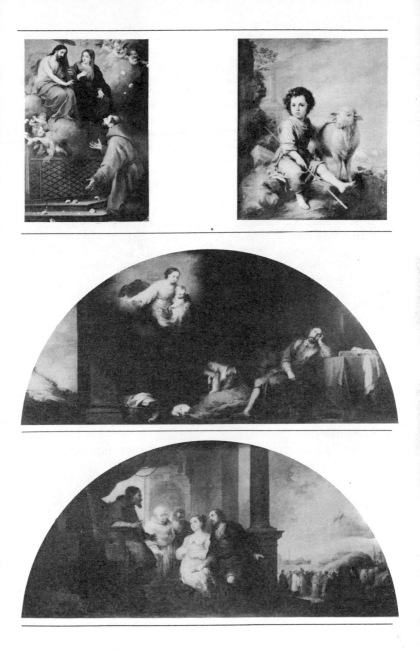

113

MURILLO, 1618-1682.

THE CONCEPTION, according to Mayer painted 1660-70 *(No. 973).* Canvas 0.91 × 0.70 m. From Isabel de Farnesio's collection. The representation of the Immaculate Virgin is one of the most popular in Murillo's production. In 1476 the Inquisition recommended this cult, and in 1483 the pope, Sixtus IV, blessed and dedicated the Sixtine Chapel to it. Murillo's success with representations of the Immaculate Conception should thus be seen in the framework of this religious-popular fashion. The later mass production of these models that go all the way to the scagliola, has bee the cause of the underestimation of the Sevillian master. Lit. Gaya Nuño (No. 94, p. 94).

MURILLO, 1618-1682.

THE IMMACULATE CONCEPTION "FROM THE ESCORIAL", about 1656-60 *(No. 972).* Canvas 2.06 × 1.44 m. Acquired by Charles IV. In the Casita of the Escorial and later in Aranjuez. Lit. Gaya Nuño (No. 70, p. 92).

THE IMMACULATE CONCEPTION "FROM ARANJUEZ" (No. 974). Canvas 2.22 × × 1.18 m. Came from Aranjuez in 1818. Lit. Gaya Nuño (No. 71, p. 92).

MURILLO, 1618-1682.

THE IMMACULATE CONCEPTION "FROM SOULT", about 1678 *(No. 2809).* Canvas 2.74 × 1.90 m. Came from Paris to the Museum in 1941.

Painted for Murillo's friend Justino de Neve for the church of the Hospital de Venerables Sacerdotes in Seville founded by him. In 1813 it was removed from Spain by the French marshal Soult. When he died, the Louvre acquired it at a public auction in 1852. Included in an exchange of art works that the French government arranged, arrived in Madrid in 1940. The composition may be considered one of the best Murillo painted of this subject. Lit. Gaya Nuño (No. 311, p. 113).

JUAN DE VALDES LEAL.

Born in Seville in 1622. In his youth he worked in Cordoba. After a journey to Madrid he returned to Seville in 1656 and died there on October 14, 1960. Lit. Trapier, E. de Gúe, *"Valdés Leal"*, New York, 1960; A. de Beruete, *"Valdés Leal"*, Madrid, 1911.

JESUS DEBATING WITH THE DOCTORS, signed and dated 1686 *(No. 1161).* Canvas 2.00 × 2.15 m. Bought from D. Luis de Echebarría by royal order of June 8, 1880. Valdés Leal's work must be seen in Seville, as examples of his work are few and recently acquired in the Prado. In the great scenery of his paintings, the Spanish Baroque tradition reaches moments of surprise and volatile explosions of great colour. Lit. Trapier (illust. 157, p. 69).

VALDES LEAL, 1622-1690.

A MARTYR OF THE ORDER OF ST. JEROME (No. 2582). Canvas 2.49 × 1.30 m. Principal painting in a series made for the church of Santa Isabel in Seville. Acquired with state subsidy in 1935 from D. Apolinar Sánchez Villalba by the Museum Foundation. Lit. Trapier (illust. 38, p. 16).

ST. JEROME. Signed *(No. 2593).* Canvas 2.11 × 1.31 m. Acquired in January of 1936 from the house of Agnew in London with funds from the bequest of the count of Cartagena. Like No. 2582 it was painted for the church of Santa Isabel in Seville and is the main work a series. It belonged to Louis Philip's collection. Lit. Trapier (illust. 37, p. 16).

JUAN CARREÑO MIRANDA.

Born in Avilés in March 25, 1614. In 1671 court painter for Charles II. He died in Madrid on October 3, 1685. Lit. Berjano Escobar, Daniel, *"El pintor D. Juan Carreño"*, Madrid; Barenttini Fernández, Jesús, *"Juan Carreño"*, 1972.

CHARLES II (No. 642). Canvas 2.01 × 1.41 m. The Berlin Museum has a copy of this painting signed in 1673. In 1734 in the Alcázar.

Charles II was the son of Philip IV and queen Mariana de Austria. He was born on November 6th, 1661, and died en November 1st, 1700. The great lesson of Velázquez is seen in all the important painters who were his contemporaries. Along with the style of objectivity and the freedom of the brush strokes in Carreño's painting, there is an opulence of colour and a lightening of the palette which may be due to the influence of Rubens. Carreño's royal portraits with their sumptuous Baroque decoration frame the almost spectral figures of the tremendous royal personages. Carreño was appointed court painter in 1669.

CARREÑO, 1614-1685.

CHARLES II, about 1680 *(No. 648)*. Canvas 0.75 × 0.60 m. For the first time in the 1746 inventory of the Isabel de Farnesio collection, ascribed to Claudio Coello.

With wonderful frankness Carreño shows us the King's abnormal face without the fragile delicacy of youth. The almost spectral countenance of the monarch is like an apparition, the sad result of so much consanguineous marriage.

CARREÑO, 1614-1685.

THE DUKE OF PASTRANA, painted after 1666 *(No. 650).* Canvas 2.17 × 1.55 m. Acquired in 1896 in the auction of the house of Osuna. Sánchez Cantón and Allende-Salazar have identified the gentleman as D. Gregorio de Silva Mendoza y Sandoval, duke of Pastrana and of Estremera, prince of Melito and Eboli and count of Saldaña. He was born in Pastrana on March 22, 1640. In 1666 he was invested with the Order of Santiago and on May 11, 1693, he became a knight of the Order of the Golden Fleece. He died on November 10, 1963. We notice in this work, apart from a clear view of the person, a certain emphasis on current fashion and an inclination towards elegance as in Van Dyck's models.

CARREÑO, 1614-1685.

PETER IWANOWITZ POTEMKIN, RUSSIAN AMBASSADOR, painted about 1681-82 *(No. 645).* Canvas 2.04 × 1.20 m. In 1680 in the court painter's workshop in the Palace. In 1701 in the Zarzuela.

Peter Iwanowitz, governor of Borousk, was in Spain twice, the first time in 1667, the second in 1681. Then he was portrayed by Carreño.

CARREÑO, 1614-1685.

ST. SEBASTIAN, 1656. Signed and dated *(No. 649).* Canvas 1.71 × 1.68 m. To the Prado from the Trinidad Museum. Ponz cites it as having been in the convent in Vallecas.

ST. ANNE GIVING LESSONS TO THE VIRGIN. Signed and dated illegibly *(No. 651).* Canvas 1.96 × 1.68 m. To the Prado from the Trinidad Museum. It may be the painting which Palomino says was in the convent of the Carmelitas Descalzas of the Court.

PAINTING UNDER THE BOURBONS

P. LOPEZ DE OSABA

The process of the decay of Spain is marked by the Treaty of the Pyrenees in 1659 and the marriage of Philip IV's daughter Maria Teresa to Louis XIV of France. One had to wait the death of Charles II (on November 1, 1700) before the process was completed.

This process of decline is amply illustrated in the painting of Carreño, the last great court painter of the Hapsburgs. In 1700 came a new monarch, who was descended from the Grand Dauphin: Philip V (1683-1746), duke of Anjou. The new King came from a country that was refined, rich, and affable to one that was poor, gloomy, and austere, worn out by so many wars, decimated and sunk to very low prestige. The Court changed its face radically. The Hapsburg austerity and its strict taste were exchanged for a pleasant, courtly life in the French style. The change in the world of painting did not lag far behind. Portraits and religious paintings were characteristic of the Hapsburg court. Both genres attained peaks that were difficult to surpass. The sumptuous, often superficial like at Court and a certain imitating Classicism praising opulence and established power are the marks of the new trend. Philip V was not able to understand the Spanish artistic vein. He therefore surrounded himself with French artists. The Royal Academy of Fine Arts was founded under Ferdinand VII (1808-1833). Art now became a guided production and the teaching of art remained codified. The Rome Prize, for the foremost artists, was established. In the field of architecture a sad occurrence —the fire in the Alcázar in Madrid in 1734— helped strengthen the French influence and the general preference of the Bourbon monarchs for the international Baroque. The project for the new royal residence was entrusted to Juvara and, after his death, to his pupil Sacchetti. The fresco paintings in the new Palace were executed mainly by foreign painters: Giaquinto, Mengs, Tiepolo. In accordance with European custom, glass, porcelain, and tapestry factories were founded to supply the royal residences with their production. Madrid already had the Santa Barbara factory of tapestry. It was, however, languishing away without any major preoccupations other than copying. Mengs (1728-1779) proposed contracting with young painters to supply the factory with original works. Bayeu, an assistant to Mengs, signed up for this new work. His brother Ramón accompanied him, and shortly after they were joined by their brother-in-law, Francisco de Goya.

Presently, the painters of this period marked a radical revolution in Spanish painting. Outstanding among them were Luis Eugenio Menéndez (1716-1780); Salvador Maella (1739-1819); Antonio Carnicero (1748-1814); Francisco Bayeu (1734-1795) who was an important representative of the strict academic style; and above all Luis Paret (1746-1799), the most affable and Frenchified of Spanish painters, who was an example of technical precision. With Goya (1746-1828) Spanish painting once more reached the highest peak. It has been said that Goya has known how to look at the disorder of reality in the world. While other masters of his day interpreted death as a glorious step to another and better life as depicted in brilliant frescos in the domes of churches and in the panelled ceilings of the halls and stairways of the palaces, Goya's scenes of death and the profane visions of his "caprichos" are loaded with a strong pressimism and existential fear that make him a premature foreunner for what is to be seen in Europe in the 20thC.

BIBLIOGRAPHY

Lafuente Ferrari, E.: *"Breve historia de la pintura española"*, Madrid, 1953.

Lafuente Ferrari, E.: *"El Museo del Prado, pintura española s. XVII y XVIII"*, Madrid, 1968.

Mayer, A. L.: *"Geschichte der Spanischen Malerei"*, Leipzig, 1922.

Sánchez Cantón, F. J.: *"El Museo del Prado"*, Madrid, 1949.

Sánchez Cantón, F. J.: *"Escultura y pintura del s. XVIII"*, vol. XVII, Ars Hispaniae, Madrid, 1965.

LUIS PARET.

Born in Madrid on February 11, 1746. He travelled in France and Italy. On November 29, 1798, he died in Madrid.

MASKET BALL (No. 2875). Wood 0.40 × 0.51 m. Acquired in November 1944 by the Museum Foundation with funds from the bequest of the count of Cartagena.

With Paret, Spanish painting took a new turn, which in the end was brought by the Monarchy in 1700 with the person of Philip V. As duke of Anjou he arrived in Spain, the antithesis of France in those days. The new Monarchy introduced French art. Luis Paret's paintings are a splendid exponent of its courtly and secularized elegance and classical contents.

LUIS PARET, 1746-1798.

THE ROYAL PAIRS, signed and dated 1773 *(No. 1044).* Canvas 2.32 × 3.65 m. The painting came from Aranjuez.

It shows a festival celebrated in Aranjuez in 1773.

FRANCISCO DE GOYA.

Born in Fuentetodos on March 30, 1746. In April 1771 in Rome. Mentioned in the Academy of Parma competition. On July 5, 1780, he was elected academician in Madrid. Court painter to Charles IV. On April 16, 1828, he died in Bordeaux. Lit. Mayer, A. L., *"Francisco de Goya"*, Barcelona, 1924; Sánchez Cantón, F. J., *"Vida y obra de Goya"*, Madrid, 1951; Sambricio, *"Tapices de Goya"*, Madrid, 1948; Hetzer, T., *"Francisco de Goya und die Krise der Kunst um 1800"* (in Aufsätze und Vortrage I. Darmstadt, 1957); Huxley, Aldous, *"The Complete Etchings of Goya"*, London, 1943; Malraux, André, *"Saturno - Essai sur Goya"*, London, 1957; Lafuente Ferrari, E., *"Goya Sämtliche Radierungen und Lithographien"*, Vienna and Munich, 1961; Ortega y Gasset, J., *"Goya"*, Madrid, 1958; Salas, F. J. *"Precisiones sobre la pintura de Goya"* (Archivo Español de Arte No. 161); Malraux, André, *"Les Dessins de Goya au Prado"*, Geneva, 1947; Gudiol, J., *"Goya"*, Barcelona, 1970.

THE HUNTING PARTY, 1775 *(No. 2857)*. Canvas 2.90 × 2.26 m. From 1775 a 1792 Goya made various series of cartoons for the production of tapestries that were to decorate the salons in the royal Palaces. The subjects have a popular root. Lit. Gudiol (No. 56), Sambricio (No. 6).

GOYA, 1746-1828.

THE PARASOL (No. 773). Canvas 1.04 × 1.52 m. The painting was delivered on August 12, 1777. It was to go above the door of the dining room in El Pardo. The tapestry is not preserved.

This marvellous piece stands out among the whole productions from 1777. Goya had been working in this genre for two years. He here attained a grace and freshness that are truly masterful. Completely in 18thC style, the painting demonstrates Goya's great talent for colour. Lit. Gudiol (No. 67), Sambricio (No. 15).

GOYA, 1746-1828.

CHARLES III (No. 737). Canvas 2.10 × 1.27 m. Three copies of this painting are known; one, considered by Beruete to be the best, belongs to the dukes of Fernán Núñez; another to the Banco Exterior in Madrid; the third is the present painting.

Son of Philip V and Isabel de Farnesio, Charles III was born in Madrid on January 20, 1716. He was, first, duke of Parma, then from 1738 King of the two Sicilys, and finally, from 1759, King of Spain. He died in Madrid on December 14, 1778. Lit. Gudiol (No. 264), Mayer (No. 101).

GOYA, 1746-1828.

THE MEADOW OF SAN ISIDRO (No. 750). Canvas 0.44 × 0.94 m.

In a letter to his friend Zapater, Goya talks worriedly about a cartoon which he had not had time to complete (May 31, 1788). Maybe this oil painting, made for the house of Osuna, is a smaller version of this subject. It was acquired by the Museum in 1896 at the sale of the ducal house of Osuna. It is a view of Madrid from the edge of the meadow of San Isidro. With the two blocks of the church of San Francisco el Grande and the Palacio de Oriente it shows a very tipical Madrid skyline, though of unfinished character, in contrast to the delicate figures in the foreground. Lit. Gudiol (No. 252), Mayer (No. 581).

GOYA, 1746-1828.

DOÑA TADEA ARIAS DE ENRIQUEZ (No. 740). Canvas 1.90 × 1.06 m. According to Viñaza painted in 1793-94. Donated to the Museum in 1896 by the grandchildren of doña Tadea. Lit. Gudiol (No. 339), Mayer (No. 251).

GOYA, 1746-1828.

THE FAMILY OF CHARLES IV (No. 726). Canvas 2.80 × 3.36 m. Executed in Aranjuez during the spring of 1800. In 1814 in the Palace in Madrid.

Goya was 54 years old when he set out to paint the Royal Family in gala, as for an audience before the whole Court. It is at the same time an imposing and splendid proof of Goya's genius. Like Velázquez' Meninas, this portrait represents a peak in the history of painting. It has the same size as Las Meninas, the penumbra of the room and the painter's device of including himself in the group. In contrast to Las Meninas the light does not center on any figure but falls obliquely at the feet of the group, thus illuminating everyone with its reflection. The composition is not contrived, but its psychological axis is heightened by the dominating figure of queen María Luisa. Stupidity, resentment, haughtiness, and sweet, child-like expressions, become visible in turn in the eyes of the persons, who appear like repeated visions. The now gentle, now daring strokes of Goya's brush transmits the splendour of the jewels, the laces and velvets, the gauzes and silks, and the decorations are fugitive lightnings in a marvellously fast and bold execution. From left to right: Don Carlos María Isidro; Goya; the Crown Prince (later King Ferdinand VII); doña María Josefa; the future wife of Ferdinand VII with her face turned away because one still did not know who she would be; doña María Isabel; Queen María Luisa; Don Francisco de Paula; King Charles IV; Don Antonio Pascual; Doña Carlota Joaquina (?); Don Luis, prince of Parma and his wife, Doña María Luisa carrying their son, Carlos Luis. Lit. Gudiol (No. 434), Mayer (No. 103).

GOYA (SKETCHES), 1746-1828.

In order to paint a portrait with as many persons as No. 726, Goya was obliged to make a series of individual sketches of the persons who were to compose the group. In passing, he made notes of colours, dresses, decorations, and fabrics. They are all the result of direct observation of the model. For that reason they are of great interest.

INFANTA DOÑA MARIA JOSEFA (No. 729). Canvas 0.74 × 0.60 m.

Daughter of Charles III and María Josefa Amalia of Satony. Born at Gaeta July 16, 1744. Died unmarried on December 8, 1801 in Madrid. Lit. Gudiol (No. 429), Mayer (No. 115).

GOYA, 1746-1828.

DON GASPAR MELCHOR DE JOVELLANOS (No. 3236). Canvas 2.05 × 1.34 m. On May 18, 1974, bought by the General Administration of Fine Arts.

Painted in Aranjuez in 1798. The dark background with the sketchy outline of Minerva, goddess of Arts and Sciences, heightens the figure of the great politician and man of letters. He is seated in the foreground leaning an elbow on his ministerial desk. The whole figure breathes a deep nostalgia and even desillusion, weariness, absorption, and discouragement because of the failure of projected reforms that were never carried out. Jovellanos (1744-1811) admired Goya who responded by leaving us this masterly portrait. Whit its rapid, well aimed brush strokes, exquisite range of colour, and profound introspection, the painting becomes a deep meditation on its era.

GOYA, 1746-1828.

CARDINAL LUIS MARIA DE BORBON Y VALLABRIGA (No. 738). Canvas 2.14 × 1.36 m. The cardinal was born in Cadalso de los Vidrios (Madrid) on May 22, 1777, as son of the Infante Cardinal D. Luis Antonio (Philip V's grandson) and doña María Teresa de Vallabriga. He was count of Chinchón, cardinal and archbishop of Toledo. He died in Madrid on March 19, 1823. The first copy of this painting, which belonged to the marquis of Acapulco, is today in the Sao Paulo Museum (Brazil). The Prado copy was sent to the Museum in 1906 by the Minister of State. Lit. Gudiol (No. 448), Mayer (No. 176).

GOYA, 1746-1828.

THE CLOTHED MAJA AND THE NAKED MAJA (Nos. 741 and 742). Canvas 0.95 ×
× 1.90 and 0.97 × 1.90 m. Mentioned with certainty for the first time in the
January 1, 1808, in the catalogue of the paintings belonging tó Godoy. There
they are called gipsies.

Probably painted in 1797-98. It seems beyond doubt that the duchess of Alba
did not serve as model. The paintings came to the Museum from the Academy
by royal decree on September 12, 1901. Much ink has been spilt over these
two works. For the moment the problem of identifying the model is insoluble.

Lit. Gudiol (Nos. 540 and 539), Mayer (Nos. 624 and 625).

Goya was denounced to the Inquisition. On May 16, 1815, he made a deposition about the figures in question and about the person who commissioned the paintings, but that document has been lost. The paintings shows. Goya's feminine ideal. Furthermore, the value of this work is increased by the almost total absence of nudes in Spanish painting. (A notable exception is Velázquez' extraordinary painting "The Rokeby Venus" in the National Gallery in London.) Of Goya's two Majas, the naked one is more painstakingly drawn, while the dressed one is much bolder.

GOYA, 1746-1828.

THE 2ND OF MAY, 1808, IN MADRID: THE FIGHT WITH THE MAMELUKES (No. 748). Canvas 2.66 × 3.45 m.

THE 3RD OF MAY, 1808, IN MADRID: THE SHOOTINGS ON THE MOUNTAIN OF PRINCIPE PIO (No. 749). Canvas 2.76 × 3.45 m. Listed in the 1872 catalogue of the Prado. Beroqui suggests that these two canvases were made after March 9, 1814. On that date the regency granted Goya 1.500 *reales* as an aid to commemorate the heroic acts of the Spanish people against the French invaders. They left the Prado on November 21, 1936. While they were being transported from Valencia to Barcelona, they were lacerated in a truck accident. They have been restored and lined, but the lost parts were not redone. The painting depicts the united heroic action of the people of Madrid, without any particular leading figure. It is a haymn of genius, devoid of the prevailing academicism.

"How the Spaniards attack the French on May 2nd, and how the French execute the Spaniards on the 3rd. ... Here is the commoner who, in the night of the shoortings, raises his two arms up high while the light from the lantern falls on his shirt. Shaggy, almost black, grotesque and sublime, ape and archangel, anonymous and inmortal, to us this Madrid rebel is the Revolution. I don't mean to say just the Political Revolution. He is that, but he is also the revolution of culture and art, the revolution which the past wants to shoot down, but cannot. What anecdote do we see in this painting? An execution. What ideology do we see? The opposite, an apotheosis, a triumphal shout of Liberty. Never has a paintings been done with so much liberty. Never has any tradition been broken with so openly, so violenty. Nakedly, irrationally, life itself pulsates here." E. d'Ors, *Tres Horas en el Museo del Prado*. Lit. Gudiol (Nos. 627 and 624), Mayer (Nos. 72 and 74).

137

GOYA, 1746-1828 (PAINTINGS FROM LA QUINTA DEL SORDO).

A MANOLA: DOÑA LEOCADIA ZORRILLA (No. 754). Mural transferred to canvas 1.47 × 1.32 m.

According to Iriarte and the inventory from "La Quinta", this is a portrait of the mother of Rosario-Weiss, doña Leocadia Zorrilla. Goya decorated his house, La Quinta del Sordo (the house of the deaf), with fourteen murals, executed between February 27, 1819, and September 17, 1823. In 1860 "La Quinta" belonged to M. R. Caumont and in 1873 to the German banker, baron Emile d'Erlanger. This latter ordered the murals to be transferred to canvas, a task carried out by D. Salvador Martínez Cubells. Without great success they were exhibited at the Paris World's Fair in 1878. The baron finally donated them to the Prado on December 20, 1881. The present painting was next to the door fo the dining room. Lit. Gudiol (No. 599), Mayer (No. 559A).

GOYA, 1746-1828.

PILGRIMAGE TO THE SPRING OF SAN ISIDRO (THE INQUISITION) (No. 775). Mural transferred to canvas 1.23 × 2.66 m

The painting was in the living room on the first floor of "La Quinta", facing nos. 757 and 758, below. The series belongs to the so-called "Black Paintings". Like the caprichos, they are a marvellous anticipation of what art has come to be in our day. The crowd of shocking figures passing by —monsters, witches, monks, rabble— exhibit the most dreadful feeling of pessimism that ever been shown in any cycle of painting, except for the religious visions of Bosch. Goya is the first to see the world's chaos, in the midst of Rococo idyl. He brings a great change to the history of art. His figures are no longer the inheritance from the Greek cosmos or from Christianity. Rather, they "stand alone before nothingness", "lost in horrible infinity" (Th. Hetzer). They are wrapped in fearful darkness, without any ray of light to console them —as happens in Rembrandt's paintings. There is no hope. In no. 767, *Half Buried Dog*, everything has come to its end. These terrible paintings ought to be called profane visions, full of restlessness, precursors of a whole epoch going to take hold of humanity in the 20thC. Lit. Gudiol (No. 713), Mayer (No. 559B).

GOYA, 1746-1828.

THE PILGRIMAGE TO SAN ISIDRO (No. 760). 1.40 × 4.38 m. Mural transferred to canvas. The painting was in the dining room of "La Quinta", facing No. 761. Lit. Gudiol (No. 703), Mayer (No. 559G).

GOYA, 1746-1828.

THE COVEN (SABBATH SCENE) (No. 761). 1.40 × 4.38 m. Mural transferred to canvas. The painting was in the dining room of "La Quinta", facing No. 760. Lit. Gudiol (No. 700), Mayer (No. 559H).

GOYA, 1746-1828.

TWO OLD PEOPLE EATING (No. 762). 0.53 × 0.85 m. Mural transferred to canvas. Bought by Don José Salamanca before "La Quinta" came into the hands of baron d'Erlanger. The baron was able to rejoin it with the other paintings. It was in the living room on the first floor of "La Quinta". Lit. Gudiol (No. 707), Mayer (No. 559I).

GOYA, 1746-1828.

DON JUAN BAUTISTA DE MUGUIRO (No. 2898). Canvas 1.03 × 0.84 m.

To the right is written: "D. Juan de Muguiro by his friend Goya, painted in his 81 year in Bordeaux. May 1827." The financier from Navarra was born in 1786. He became a friend of Goya's in Bordeaux. This wonderful testimony from Goya's last period was a bequest to the Museum from the second count of Muguiro, a nephew of the one in the portrait. It came to the Prado at the death of the third count, Don Fermín, in 1946, in whose possession it had been. Lit. Gudiol (No. 762), Mayer (No. 361).

GOYA, 1746-1828.

THE MILKMAID FROM BORDEAUX (No. 2899). Canvas 0.74 × 0.68 m. Signed.

This painting is mentioned in a letter from doña Leocadia Zorrilla on December 9, 1829. It was then acquired by Don Juan B. Muguiro. Don Fermín de Muguiro willed it to the Museum in 1946. It is an extraordinary three-quarter figure portrait, showing the old master's fluent style and exquisite colour. Lit. Gudiol (No. 767), Mayer (No. 361).

ROBERT CAMPIN.

"The master of Flémalle". About 1378-79 to 1444.

It is today believed that a "Rogier de la Pasture", assistant in Campin's workshop, was Roger van der Weyden. In Campin's work the delicate Gothic style was followed by a new realism, in which many details of nature obtained a higher symbolic meaning, recognised particulary by E. Panofsky. It cannot be traced out whether Robert Campin in Tournai or Jan van Eyck in Bruges was the first to accomplish this change towards realism. Lit. Friedländer[2], vol. II, 1967.

ST. JOHN THE BAPTIST AND THE FRANCISCAN BROTHER HEINRICH VON WERL (No. 1513). ST. BARBARA (No. 1514). Wooden panel 1.01 × 0.47 m each.

Acquired by Charles IV. They represent two doors of a triptych of which the central part has been lost. It is Campin's only dated work: 1438. At the lower edge of the painting is written: Anno milleno centum quater decem ter de octo hic fecit effigiem... depingi minister henricus werlis magister coloniensis". The donor is praying in front of an open door leading into the central (lost) panel. The tower in the open countryside behind the right window indicates that the virgin seated with her back to the lit fireplace is St. Barbara and not Mary. The theologian Werl participated in the Council of Basel in 1453. He was in Tournai in 1453 and died in 1461 in Osnabrück. Lit. Friedländer[2], 1967, No. 67.

CAMPIN, about 1378/79-1444.

THE ANNUNCIATION (No. 1915). Wooden panel 0.76 × 0.70 m. In Philip II's collection.

This painting is more likely to be attributed to one of Campin's fellow-workers like Jacques Daret than to Campin himself. The Church is here interpreted as a new covenant made possible by Mary who is praying in the church. The angel is approaching from outside where a statue of David is standing as representative of the old covenant. Lit.: Friedländer[2], 1967, No. 52.

JAN VAN EYCK, about 1385-1441. Active in Bruges. In 1428-29 travel to Portugal. *THE FOUNTAIN OF MERCY AND THE TRIUMPH OF THE CHURCH OVER THE SYNAGOGUE (No. 1511, replica).* Wooden panel 1.81 × 1.16 m. From the convent of los Jerónimos in Segovia where it was already in 1454.

Given the fact that the replicas are preserved only in Spain, as the original may have been in earlier times, it is possible that the panel was painted during van Eyck's journey to Portugal in 1429. The painting has the name of the spring painted on it in which Hosts float in the water of life. In the lower left corner the Church, represented by the Christian classes, led by emperor, pope, king, and duke. To the right the Synagogue is led by the High Priest with his eyes covered. In the center are twelve angel musicians, and above God, Father and Son, on a throne decorated with the figures of the prophets. Between Mary and St. John the Evangelist, at the feet of the Allmighty is the Lamb. The composition in the painting is a variation of the theme in the altar in Ghent.

FOLLOWER OF JAN VAN EYCK.
MARY WITH THE CHILD (No. 2696). Wooden panel 0.18 × 0.15 m. Pablo Bosch bequest No. 64.

ROGER VAN DER WEYDEN (Roger de la Pasture). About 1399-1464.
Born in Tournai. In 1427 he used the name "Rogelet de la Pasture, natif de Tournai" *(sic)*. He worked together with Campin. In 1432 he was known as "maitre Roger de la Pasture", the name under which future times were to know him. From 1436 until his death "City Painter" in Brussels. In 1450 travel to Italy. Lit.: M. J. Friedländer, Vol. II², 1967. M. Davies, *"Roger van der Weyden"*, London and Munich, 1972.

DESCENT FROM THE CROSS (No. 2825). Wooden panel 2.20 × 2.62 m. Done about 1435 for the Chapel of the Crossbowmakers. Acquired by Mary of Hungary before 1548. In 1574 Philip II brought it to the Escorial. In 1937 by the Prado exchanged for a copy by Coxcie.

This major work is the first of Roger's theological interpretations of the events of the Holy Mass by a painted altarpiece. Christ is presented to the faithful, like the sacrament, taken down from the cross. The scene is placed inside a gothic shrine. The three persons to the left, including St. John, and the three persons to the right, including Mary Magdalene, are shifted to either side so as not to cover the Body of Christ. The Virgin Mary has fainted below the cross. Her limbs, arms and legs repeat the position of Christ's limbs; she only keeps her head up. Mary can thus be seen as "co-Redeemer" participating in the work of salvation. The cranium and bones of Adam remind of his being buried at Golgotha whence he will be resurrected because Jesus died on the Cross. The overall realism of the painting serves as an illustration of the spirituality of the subject. Lit.: Friedländer, 1967, No. 3. Davies, p. 87ff.

VAN DER WEYDEN. About 1399-1464.
PIETA (No. 2540). Wooden panel 0.47 × 0.35 m. Acquired by the Museum Foundation in 1925.

There is a replica of this subject in Berlin and copies with variations in London and Brussels. Of these, the London version is the best. However, the Madrid panel was painted in Roger's workshop with Roger himself working on it extensively. The arched upper part was added about or after 1500. Lit. Friedländer, 1967, No. 3. Davies p. 85. José María Cabrera, *"La Piedad de Roger van der Weyden"*, laboratory analysis. Bol. del M. del Prado, T. I, No. I, 1980, p. 39f.

VAN DER WEYDEN. About 1399-1464.

VIRGIN WITH THE CHILD (No. 2722). Wooden panel 1.00 × 0.52 m. Fernández-Durán bequest 1930.

The Virgin Mary is, against all tradition, dressed in red. Above her an angel is holding a crown. She is seated like a gothic sculpture in a niche with the Child reading on her lap. She seems elevated and thus separated from the world. This panel belongs to the most perfect creations of Roger. Lit.: Friedländer II², 1967, supplement 132. Davies, p. 90.

VAN DER WEYDEN. About 1399-1464.

THE REDEMPTION (Nos. 1888, 1889, 1891). Exterior: *CAESAR'S MONEY (Nos. 1890, 1892).* Wooden panel 1.95 × 1.72 m. (central panel); 1.95 × 0.77 m. (each door).

Philip II and his son Charles donated this altar to the Convento de los Angeles in Madrid. It is the most important theological interpretation in the form of an altarpiece to come out of Roger's workshop. The central panel shows in six archivolts the Passion of Christ with the crucifixion in the middle. Simultaneously, scenes of the six sacraments are depicted on the side posts, the mass behind the Cross being the seventh. Thus the various scenes interpret the churchs space as Ecclesia and summary of Salvation and Faith. The wings complete the essential idea. On the left the seven days of Creation with the Original Sin and the Expulsion in the center. On the right the seven Works of Mercy that the Christian ought to practise in order to undergo Judgment Day, depicted in the center. The twenty-eight scenes on this altarpiece represent the complete idea of salvation of the Church. The outer wings interpret the Church's relation to the world in the words of Christ to the pharisees showing him the tax money: "Render unto Caesar that which is Caesar's and unto God that which is God's." These grisaille paintings on the outer wings were exposed on week-days. The imitation of sculpture and the representation of painted sculptures on the main part put the scenes back into the sacred sphere of high medieval art. Lit.: Friedländer[2], 1967, No. 47 (workshop?). Davies does not mention the work because of not attributing it to Roger.

VAN DER WEYDEN. About 1399-1464.

LA REDEMPTION. Exterior: *CAESAR'S MONEY* (see above).

DIERIC BOUTS. About 1420-1475.

Active in Louvain. Influenced by Roger van der Weyden and his most important follower. Lit.: Friedländer II², 1968.

ANNUNCIATION-VISITATION-ADORATION OF THE ANGELS-ADORATION OF THE MAGI (No. 1461). Triptych: Wooden panel 0.80 × 0.56 m (wings); 0.80 × 1.05 m (central panel). In Philip II's collection.

It is an early (1445) work. The pattern of this characteristic Flemish altarpiece was developed by Roger van der Weyden. The four scenes from the life of the Virgin Mary and Christ are framed by four portals, in the archivolts of which further scenes are depicted: The Annunciation left, taken from the Genesis, the other three taken from the Passion, beginning with the betrayal of Judas and ending with Pentecost.

GERARD DAVID.

Active between 1484 and 1523. Born in Oudwater. Working in Bruges, he continued the tradition of Roger van der Weyden and Memling. Lit.: Friedländer IV B², 1971.

REST DURING THE FLIGHT INTO EGYPT (No. 2643). Wooden panel 0.60 × 0.38 m. Pablo Bosch bequest No. 11. Lit.: Friedländer IV B², 1971, p. 212.

FOLLOWER OF DAVID.

VIRGIN WITH CHILD AND TWO ANGELS CROWNING HER (No. 1512). Wooden panel 0.34 × 0.27 m. Influenced by Dürer's Virgins.

THE VIRGIN MARY WITH CHILD (No. 1537). Wooden panel 0.45 × 0.34 m. To the Prado from the Escorial in 1839.

FOLLOWER OF DAVID.
THE CRUCIFIXION (No. 2542). Wooden panel 0.45 × 0.33 m. Acquired in 1928 by the Foundation for Artistic Treasure.

HANS MEMLING. About 1433-1494.
Born in Seligenstadt, near Frankfurt. Since 1465 active in Bruges. He followed the tradition of R. van der Weyden and Dirk Bouts.

NATIVITY-ADORATION OF THE KINGS-PURIFICATION (No. 1557). Triptych: 0.95 × × 1.45 m (central panel); 0.95 × 0.63 m (each wing). The triptych belonged to Charles V. In the Prado since 1847.

In its central composition and in the right wing the altarpiece follows van der Weyden's late work in Munich. The left wing shows the birth of Jesus. according to the vision of St. Bridget. The Virgin Mary is worshipping the Child lying on the end of her cape. Compared with Roger's altar, the space is wider here, the figures are smaller, their limbs more delicate, and their features softer. The composition is filled with solemn tranquility. It is a major work by Memling, painted about 1470.

MEMLING. About 1433-1494.
VIRGIN AND CHILD BETWEEN TWO ANGELS (No. 2543). Wooden panel 0.36 × × 0.26 m. Given to the Museum by the marquise of Cabrina in 1844.

A late work by Memling, damaged by restauration. Lit.: Friedländer V[2], 1971, No. 59.

THE MASTER OF "THE VIRGO INTER VIRGINES".
This master worked between 1480 and 1500. Contemporary of Geertgen's and Bosco's, like them he was Dutch.

PIETA (No. 2539). Wooden panel 0.84 × 0.78 m. Acquired in 1928 by the Museum Foundation.

It is a typical work by this important artist whose style is individual and completely independent. Lit.: Friedländer V², 1969 (copy). No. 100.

HIERONYMUS BOSCH. About 1450-1516.
Born in Hertogenbosch where he worked until his death. His works in the Prado, nos. 2822 and 2056, belong to his early period and nos. 2048 and 2049 to his last period. The rest with his major pieces, The Hay Wain and The Garden of Lusts, are of the middle period. Lit.: X. de Salas, *"El Bosco en la literatura española"*, Barcelona 1943; Ch. de Tolnay, *"Hieronymus Bosch"*, Baden-Baden 1956 and London 1966. Friedländer V², 1969.

TABLE TOP WITH THE SEVEN DEADLY SINS (No. 2822). Wood 1.20 × 1.50 m. The table belonged to Philip II.

Its top shows an exhortation. In the center of the circle stands Christ as Man of Sorrows, showing his wounds. Below him is written, "Cave, cave, Dominus videt" (Beware, beware, God sees you). In the corners are four circles representing the four final things that human beings expect: Death, Judgment Day, Hell, and Glory. Christ is looking at those who are committing the Seven Deadly Sins. Clockwise from the center they are: Ira - anger; Invidia - envy; Avaritia - avarice; Gula - gluttony; Acidia - sloth; Luxuria - lust; and Superbia - pride. It is like a world theater world of human vices shown with the greatest realism. At the same time scenes of Flemish everyday life are demonstrated. The forms used for the holy subjects —the Man of Sorrows, Judgment Day, and Paradise— are traditional whereas the Seven Deadly Sins contain new observations of nature. Lit.: Friedländer V², 1969, No. 104.

BOSCH. About 1450-1516.
THE HAY WAIN (No. 2052). Wooden panel 1.35 × 1.00 m (central panel); 1.35 × 0.45 m (each wing).

Signed: Jheronimus Bosch. On the back of the wings: THE PRODIGAL SON (The Journey of Life). An old copy is the Escorial. It belonged to Philip II. The painting shows a fatalistic interpretation of the world and includes an exhortation. The theme is based on the Flemish proverb: "The world is a mountain of hay and every man takes from it as much as he can." As in the table of the Seven Deadly Sins, Christ is also here depicted as the Man of Sorrow, contemplating what is happening in the world. All vices are being committed. On top of the hay cart a pair of lovers make music without paying attention to their surroundings, an angel prays for them and in spite of that a devil plays a flute. The painting should be "read" from left to right. To the left is shown the Beginning when the angel-devils lost Paradise in their fall. Adam and Eve and all mankind lost it through the Original Sin. Our time on earth is shown in the central panel; it is a world stage with the sea in the distance. Across this scenario diabolic creatures pull the hay cart as spoils of Hell. Men are fighting for the hay and falling under the wheels of the cart. Following the cart are the emperor and the pope, the king of France and the duke of Burgundy with all the people. The pope has the features of Alexander VI Borgia. The painting must have been made during his papacy (1492-1503) or rather at the end of it. The present, which is so full of sin, pride, and stupidity, is followed by the future in the shape of Hell, where the dead are admitted to its blazing city. This pessimistic view of the world reveals the uselessness of Christ's death on the Cross.

BOSCH. About 1450-1516.
THE HAY WAIN. Outer wings: 1.35 × 0.45 m (each).

"The Prodigal Son" on the outside of the wings shows the mankind's journey through this sinful world. The path is narrow, the bridge over the brook frail. In the background there are gallows and robbers assaulting a traveller and a couple, carelessly dancing. Since this triptych, which takes misfortune as its theme, follows the form of the altar triptychs of Salvation, it makes the stupidity of the world stand out even more clearly. Lit.: Friedländer V², 1969, No. 111.

BOSCH. About 1450-1516.
GARDEN OF LUSTS (No. 2823). Wooden panel 2.20 × 1.95 m. The triptych was in Philip II's collection.

The title does not really describe the contents of the painting. Gombrich (London) may be right in saying that the central panel represents humanity before the Original Sin, just as the theme on the closed wings of the triptych may be the world after the Flood. Less convincing is W. Fraenger's (Amsterdam) opinion that the subject is the future "Thousand year realm of happiness". This was the dream of the followers of the Adamite sect who wanted to be naked like Adam and live together in an erotic community of all men. Panofsky counters this saying that Bosch, like the foremost collector of his works, Philip II, was more a case for psychotherapy than for the Inquisition. In this world, which did not yet know Christ, men fearlessly devoted themselves to the joys of love and game. there is no distress nor sickness, nor death. On the left wing is a paradisiacal landscape: Christ leads Eve towards the awakened Adam. On the right wing there is not really Hell being depicted, but a burning world with beasts and demons tormenting men and frightening them with visions of awful horrors. In spite of all attempts to interpret the painting, its contents largely remain obscure. All we can say with certainty is that it represents the fate of mankind, and that it should be read from left to right. It is in prime state of conservation. Lit.: Friedländer V², 1969, No. 68.

BOSCH. About 1450-1516.
GARDEN OF LUSTS. Outer wings (see above).

ALBERT BOUTS. About 1460-1549.

Son of Dirk Bouts. He lived and worked in Louvain.

MAN OF SORROW (No. 2698). Wooden panel 0.30 m in diameter. Workshop piece. Pablo Bosch bequest No. 66.

DISCIPLE OF BOUTS.

MAN OF SORROW (No. 2672). Wooden panel 0.33 × 0.23 m. Pablo Bosch bequest No. 40.

QUINTIN MASSYS. 1465-1530.

Massys hailed from Louvain. He became the foremost painter of the Antwerp school. He was among the earliest Netherlandish painters to be influenced by the masters of the Italian High Renaissance.

ECCE HOMO (No. 2801). Wooden panel 1.60 × 1.20 m. Bequest from don Mariano Lanuza in 1936. Lit. Friedländer VII[2], 1971, illustration 10.

THE MASTER OF THE HOLY BLOOD.
Active in Bruges about 1520.

ECCE HOMO (No. 1559). Triptych. Central panel 1.09 × 0.89 m. Acquired by Ferdinand VII in 1829.

JAN GOSSART, CALLED MABUSE. Active between 1503 and 1533/36.
Mabuse worked mainly in Middelburg. In 1508-09 he undertook a journey to
Rome. He is among the foremost Netherlandish painters influenced by the
Italian Renaissance. His work was decisively inspired by Leonardo da Vinci.
Lit.: Friedländer VIII², 1972.

CHRIST BETWEEN THE VIRGIN MARY AND ST. JOHN THE BAPTIST (No. 1510). Wooden
panel 1.22 × 1.33 m. In Philip II's collection.

It is a free imitation of the same theme in the altar in Ghent, painted by Jan van
Eyck. The present versión is enriched by new ornamentation. Christ, in priestly
vesture, is blessing the spectator. The angel in the round section above holding
an inscription is a typical mannerist element. Lit.: Friedländer VIII², 1972, No. 19.

MABUSE, 1478 - 1533-6.
THE VIRGIN WITH THE CHILD (No. 1930). Wooden panel 0.63 × 0.50 m. In Philip II's
collection.

The painting exists in various versions. It is the wing of a diptych. However, the
difference in the background makes it unlikely that the panel in London (Man
with a Rosary) should be the right hand wing of said diptych. The work must have
been very famous because also Baldung Grien made a copy of it (now in
Nüremberg). Lit.: Friedländer VIII², No. 35.

ADRIAN ISENBRANDT. Active from 1510 to 1551.

All we know of this painter is that he worked in Bruges and shows influence first from G. David and later from Mabuse. We have a large number of paintings by him. Lit.: Friedländer XI[1], 1933.

MARY MAGDALENE (No. 2664). Wooden panel 0.45 × 0.34 m. Pablo Bosch bequest No. 32.

The expression of the saint is characteristic for Isenbrandt and shows his dependence on G. David. Lit.: Friedländer XI[1], 1933, No. 212A.

JOACHIM PATINIER OR PATINIR. Active 1515-1524.

All we know of this artist is that in 1515 he became master in Antwerp, and that in 1524 he died. Dürer coined the word "Landschaftsmaler" (landscape painter) to describe Patinier. His four paintings in the Prado are among the best in his limited production. Lit.: Friedländer IX, 1934.

REST DURING THE FLIGHT INTO EGYPT (No. 1611). Wooden panel 1.21 × 1.77 m. To the Prado from the Escorial. It may have been in Philip II's collection.

The rest during the flight into Egypt is an occasion to paint a wide landscape with peasants, soldiers, farms, and churches. Joseph is bringing milk. The figure of the Virgin Mary is inspired by the old Flemish madonnas. Lit.: Friedländer IX, 1934, No. 235.

BERNARD VAN ORLEY. 1492-1542.

Lived and worked in Brussels. Two journeys to Italy made him choose Raphael as his ideal. In 1515 court painter for the regent Margaret and after her death for Mary of Hungary. Lit.: Friedländer VIII², 1972.

THE VIRGIN GIVING BREAST (No. 1920). Wooden panel 0.54 × 0.30 m. From the Escorial to the Prado.

It follows a composition by Robert Campin and translates it into the new Romanism style. The Virgin Mary's garment has been painted with particular care. There are many copies. In Friedländer's opinion the present painting is also a copy. Lit.: Friedländer VIII², 1972, No. 125A.

ORLEY. 1492-1542.

THE VIRGIN WITH THE CHILD (No. 1932). Wooden panel 0.98 × 0.71 m. From Aranjuez to the Prado.

Painted about 1516. Our Lady sits in a bower offering a pear to the Child who plays with a rosary. The Child's posture, like that of the Child St. John the Baptist (to the right, behind the column), denotes Raphael's influence.

MARINUS VAN REYMERSWAELE. Active about 1509, died in 1567.

Born in Reymerswaele, Zeeland, apprenticed in Antwerp in 1506-09. Later he worked in Zeeland and perhaps Middelburg. His dated works go from 1521 to 1551. He was constantly repeating the same compositions, such as St. Jerome, The Money Broker and His Wife, or The Tax Collectors. He combines in his works still-lives of great accuracy with realistic portraits full of character and hands drawn with extraordinary precision. Lit.: Friedländer XII¹, 1935.

THE MONEY BROKER AND HIS WIFE (No. 2567). Wooden panel 0.38 × 0.97 m. Signed: Marinus me fecit ad 1539. Bequest to the Museum from the duke of Tarifa in 1934.

This very famous and often repeated painting is depending on a 1514 composition by Massys in the Louvre. Other examples are in Munich (1538), Nantes (1538), Copenhagen (1540), Dresden (1541), and other places. Lit.: Friedländer XII¹, 1934, No. 170.

REYMERSWAELE. About 1509-1567.

ST. JEROME (No. 2100). Wooden panel 0.75 × 1.01 m. Signed: Mdad (sic) me fecit Aº 1551. In 1636 in the Alcázar in Madrid. Lit.: Friedländer XII¹, 1935, No. 162.

JAN SANDERS VAN HEMESEN. About 1500-1564.

Born in Hemixen near Antwerp. Apprenticed to Hendrick van Cleve in Antwerp, died in Harlem. Father of the painter Catherine van Hemesen. Lit.: Friedländer XII[1], 1935.

THE SURGEON (No. 1541). Wooden panel 1.00 × 1.41 m. Before 1614 in El Pardo.

The painting done before 1555, should be seen as an allegory. It is based on the medieval idea that insanity can be cured by operating the patient and extracting a stone from his brain. Lit.: Friedländer XII[1], 1935, No. 217.

HEMESEN. About 1500-1564.

THE VIRGIN MARY AND THE CHILD (No. 1542). Wooden panel 1.35 × 0.91 m. In 1746 in La Granja. Signed with the monogram AOD 1543.

This composition of the Virgin in front of a landscape with a very high horizon is based on traditions going back to Leonardo and Raphael. Lit.: Friedländer XII[1], 1935, No. 199.

ANONYMOUS FLEMISH PAINTER. About 1510.

THE SAVIOUR (No. 2636). Wooden panel 0.34 × 0.27 m. Pablo Bosch bequest No. 3.

Friedländer has attributed the painting to a Flemish master.

PIETER BRUEGHEL "THE ELDER". About 1520-1569.
Apprenticed to Pieter Coecke van Aelst whose daughter he married in 1553.
In 1551, independent master in the Antwerp painters' guild. In Rome in 1553
and since 1554 in Antwerp, since 1563 in Brussels. Jan Brueghel "the Elder"
(Velvet Brueghel) and Pieter Brueghel "the Younger" (Hell Brueghel) were
his sons. Lit.: Friedländer XIV[1], 1937; R. Genaille, "P. Brueghel", Paris, 1953;
F. Grossman, "P. Brueghel", The paintings, London, 1955.

THE TRIUMPH OF DEATH (No. 1393). Wooden panel 1.17 × 1.62 m. First listed
in 1774 in the San Ildefonso inventory. Painted between 1560 and 1564. In Italy
Brueghel must have seen depictions of the triumph of Death. His pessimistic
view of the world found its clearest expression in this theme. It shows the
different types of death, on sea, on land, on the gallows, and in war. The dead
are killing the living, thus increasing the army of corpses. Brueghel also
wanted to demonstrate how the different classes of people in the great world
theater are carried off by death. From left to right the Emperor, the Cardinal,
the poor woman with the child, the pilgrim assassinated on his journey, the
serf, and, finally, the serene party around the table. Only the two lovers at the
right do not realize Death making music for them. The dark colors of the bare
earth and the fires in the background add to the anxiety. Lit.: Friedländer XIV[1],
1937.

PEETER HUYS. Active 1545-1581.

HELL (No. 2095). Wooden panel 0.36 × 0.82 m. Signed in 1570: peeter huys fe.
Brought to the Museum from the Escorial.

It is a late imitation of Bosch by the Antwerp painter.

GERMAN PAINTING

W. BRAUNFELS.

There was only a small group of paintings from the German school in the royal collections and hence now in the Prado. However, they are of the highest quality: 4 Dürers, 2 Baldungs, 2 Cranachs, plus two works by Ch. Amberger, and one Elsheimer, actually a small number of paintings of the German Renaissance.

There was never a tendency of the Spanish Court towards collecting German painting. Cranach's two hunting scenes belonged already to Mary of Hungary, Charles V's sister. The two Baldungs were a present to Philip II. Dürer's Adam and Eve were likewise a present from Queen Christina of Sweden to Philip IV; they had earlier been taken as war booty by Sweden in Prague. The same King acquired Dürer's self portrait from the assets of Charles I of England's collections.

Medieval German painting was beyond the orbit and comprehension of the Spanish crown. Not until the end of the 18th C was there a German, Anton Raphael Mengs, among the court painters.

ALBRECHT DÜRER. 1471-1528.
Lived in Nuremberg. In 1494-95 and 1506-07 in Venice, travelled to the Low Countries in 1520-21. Lit.: E. Panofsky, "The Life and Art of Albrecht Dürer", two volumes, 4. edition, 1955; F. Anzelewsky, "A. Dürer, Das Malerische Werk", Berlin, 1971.

SELF PORTRAIT (No. 2179). Wooden panel 0.52 × 0.41 m. After Dürer's death this painting came into the town-hall of Nuremberg. Later, via the Earl of Arundel, to King Charles I of England. Philip IV bought it from the latter's assets. The young Dürer made three self portraits. In the first, now in Paris, he was 23 years old. In the third, which is in Munich, he was 28. The middle one is the Prado portrait, painted when Dürer was 26. In his lifetime the three self portraits hung in his house in Nuremberg. They show him not as a craftsman at work but rather dressed up as a distinguished gentleman. His gesture and the gloves demonstrate he is not working. His eyes are looking straight towards the spectator. These three early works reflect Dürer's self-esteem as an independent painter. Under the splay of the window is written 1498. "Das malt ich nach meiner gestalt Ich war sex und zwanzing jor alt Albrecht Dürer." Lit.: Anzelewsky, p. 152ff.

DÜRER. 1471-1528.

UNKNOWN MAN (No. 2180). Wooden panel 0.50 × 0.36 m. The portrait was a present from the Nuremberg Council to the Earl of Arundel. In 1686 in the inventory of the Madrid Alcázar. The date has been read 1521 and 1524. The fact that it is painted on an oak panel has led to the belief that the portrait was painted during Dürer's journey to the Low Countries in 1521. However, the gentleman's clothes indicate that he is German. The background of the painting might originally have been blue. It belongs to the important series of male portraits from Dürer's last period. Lit.: Anzelewsky, p. 262.

DÜRER. 1471-1528.

ADAM AND EVE (No. 2177 and 2178). Wooden panel each 2.09 × 0.81 m. Dürer painted these two masterpieces just after his return from Venice in 1507. He had been thinking about the subject since 1500; it served as a demonstration of his studies of proportions. The influence of Venetian painting, particularly of Giorgione, is discernible in Adam's posture, in the position of his right arm, in the oblique inclination of his head with its open mouth, and in the delicately modelled body. When Prague was sacked by the Swedes during the Thirty Years' War, the paintings from Emperor Rudolph II's collection wound up in Stockholm. When Queen Christina abdicated in 1654, she gave the paintings to Philip IV. The picture with Adam has the monogram A.D., and from the branch in the painting with Eve a plaque reads:

"Albertus Dürer almanus
faciebat post virginis
partum 1507 A. D."

Lit.: Anzelewsky, p. 208ff.

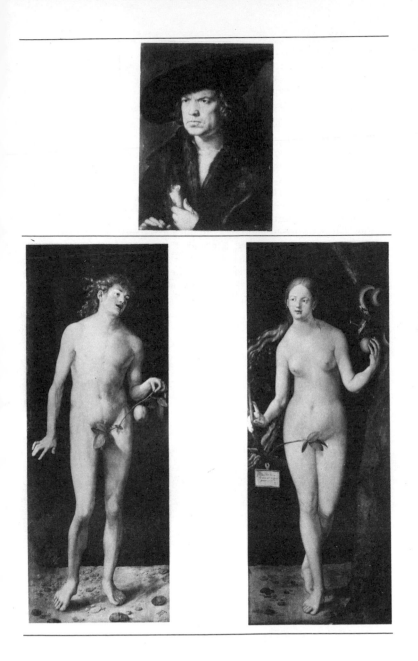

LUCAS CRANACH "THE ELDER". 1472-1553.

Born in Kronach (Franconia). Palace painter for Prince Johann Friedrich in Wittenberg. He died in Weimar. Lit.: M. J. Friedländer and J. Rosenberg, *"Die Gemälde von Lukas Cranach"*, 1932.

HUNT IN HONOUR OF CHARLES V IN FRONT OF HARTENFELS PALACE NEAR TOR-GAU (Nos. 2175 and 2176). Wooden panel 1.14 × 1.75 and 1.18 × 1.77 m. Signed and dated 1544.

They probably came into the possession of Mary of Hungary, Charles V's sister, as a present from the imprisoned elector. The younger Cranach also worked on these paintings. Two phases of the aristocratic deer hunt are depicted in front of the palace of Hartenfels near Torgau, a hunt that never took place. No. 2175 shows the south wing of the palace, which was completed in 1536. No. 2176 shows the north wing, completed in 1544. It has not been possible to identify all the aristocrats. In no. 2175, to the left, Johann Friedrich and Charles V are identified with certainty, although they never hunted together. In no. 2176 we see, among others, Ferdinand I of Austria and again Johann Friedrich; they likewise can never have hunted together. To the right in both paintings we see Sybila of Saxony, the wife of the prince elector, with a crossbow.

LUKAS CRANACH "THE ELDER". 1472-1553.

HUNT IN HONOUR OF CHARLES V IN FRONT OF HARTENFELS PALACE, NEAR TOR-GAU (No. 2176). Wooden panel 1.18 × 1.77 m. (see above).

HANS BALDUNG GRIEN. 1484/85-1545.

This great humanist painter from Strassburg son of a learned man, found his style under Dürer's influence. He was Dürer's assistant from 1502 to 1505.

THE THREE GRACES (No. 2219). THE THREE AGES AND DEATH (No. 2220). Wooden panel, each 1.51 × 0.61 m. Possession of Philip II.

They are late works of Baldung's, painted about 1540, interpreted in various ways: as the allegories "The Heavenly Flower of Youth" and "The transience of Life on Earth"; as "Life" and "Death"; and as "Humanity Before and After the Fall", to which the Christ above the Death alludes. The Graces should be seen as goddesses of Music. The swan is a symbol of music because of its pretty song.

CHRISTOPH AMBERGER. 1500/10-1561/62.

Leading master of his time in Augsburg.

JÖRG ZÖRER, GOLDSMITH IN AUGSBURG (No. 2183). Wooden panel 0.78 × × 0.51 m. 1746 in La Granja.

The inscription has the date MCXXXI and the age of the man, AETATIS XXXI. The coat of arms on the ring belongs to the Zörer family.

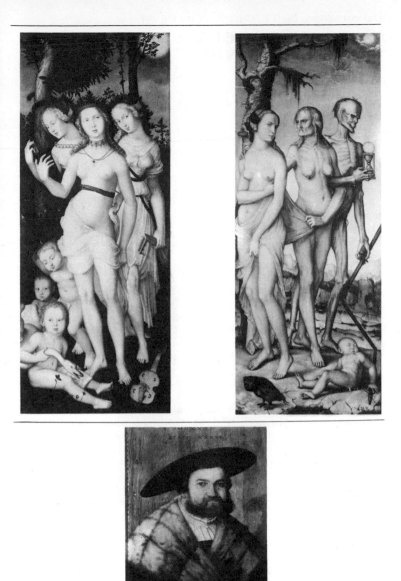

ITALIAN PAINTING OF THE 14TH AND 15TH CENTURY

L. DUSSLER.

Whoever looks at the collection of paintings in the Prado knows, as long as he is not totally ignorant, that the Museum's greatest treasure are the Italian masters from the 16thC. Within that century the Venetian painters are the ones who are best represented both quantitatively and qualitatively.

On the other hand, the collection of Italian masters from the 14thC and 15thC does not compare in quantity to the brilliant paintings by the Flemish masters.

This is due to the interest of the Hapsburgs as collectors. The Emperor Maximilian I and Margaret, who was governor of the Low Countries, concentrated all their patronage of art and joyful admiration of it on the old Flemish and German painters. Therefore, with very few exceptions the paintings by primitive Tuscans today in the Prado were bequeathed to the Museum in our century. Thus the interesting panels from the workshop of Giotto's great disciple, Taddeo Gaddi; the exquisite panel showing the liberal arts by G. Da Ponte, and, finally, Botticelli's cassone panel illustrating the Decameron. All of these were a gift from the great Spanish collector F. Cambó.

That 17thC Spanish sovereigns were open to the value of old Italian art is shown both by Fra Angelico's beautiful "Annunciation" with its predella panels, and by A. Mantegna's incomparable "Death the Virgin". This painting came directly from Mantua via Charles I of England's collections. If the Prado had no more than this creation of Italian art, the art lover ought to do everything possible, without heeding the difficulties, to know the original.

Due to a unique circumstance it became possible a few years ago to exhibit the "Death of the Virgin" in the same galley as the "Dead Christ" by Mantegna's contemporary, Antonello da Messina. With the acquisition of the latter painting the quality of the Museum's collection was definitely improved.

The foremost painter of the old Venetian school, Giovanni Bellini, is also represented. His remarkable work "Devotion" may show only one aspect of his many facetted world; however, it does afford a comprehension for measuring how close his art is to that of the Cinquecento.

TADDEO GADDI. Died in 1366.
Born in Florence, first apprentice, later collaborator of Giotto's. Active mainly in Florence.

ST. ELIGIUS IN THE GOLDSMITH'S WORKSHOP (No. 2842). Wooden panel 0.35 × × 0.39 m. Part of a predella like no. 2841. Bequeathed to the Museum in 1941 by F. Cambó.

The marvellous panels with scenes from the life of the patron saint of the goldsmiths are listed here under the name of Giotto's great disciple. However, several signs point to the same style as that of an unknown master who has been called the "Maestro della Madonna della Misericordia".

GADDI.
ST. ELIGIUS BEFORE KING CHLOTAR (No. 2841). Wooden panel 0.35 × 0.39 m. Like no. 2841, part of a predella. Bequeathed to the Museum in 1941 by F. Cambó.

GIOVANNI DA PONTE. 1385-1437.
Florentine painter probably apprenticed to Spinello Aretino. Influenced by Fra Angelico, Masaccio and Lorenzo Monaco.

THE SEVEN LIBERAL ARTS (No. 2844). Wooden panel 0.56 × 1.55 m. Bequeathed to the Museum in 1941 by F. Cambó.

In the center on the throne is Astronomy. Ptolemy sits at her feet. From the center to the left: Rethoric guided by Cicero; Dialectic at the hand of Aristotle, and Grammar with two children accompanied by Donato. To the right are Geometry holding the hand of Euclid, Arithmetic with Phythagoras, and finally Music with Tubulcain. The panel, part of a cassone, is the same as a work with ladies and gentlemen in the Musée André in Paris. About 1425-30.

FRA ANGELICO, CALLED IL BEATO ANGELICO. About 1386-1455.

Dominican monk in the convent of St. Dominic in Fiesole. He worked in Florence in the convent of St. Mark, in Rome, in Cortona, and in Orvieto. He started as a miniature painter in G. Starnina's studio. Later influenced by Masolino. Lit.: M. Salmi, "Problemi dell' Angelico", in: Commentari I, 1950 fac. II, p. 75ff; J. Pope-Hennessy, "Fra Angélico", London 1952.

THE ANNUNCIATION (No. 15). Wooden panel 1.94 × 1.94 m. Predella panels: the Betrothal, the Visitation, the Adoration of the Kings, the Presentation in the Temple, and the Death of Mary. From the convent of St. Dominic in Fiesole. In 1611 it belonged to the duke of Lerma who gave it to the Dominicans in Valladolid.

The theme was painted many times by Fra Angelico on panels and as frescos. The pleasing composition particularly resembles the painting of the Virgin in Cortona. This panel is undoubtedly based on a variation of the model created by the master. Like the scenes in the predella panels, however, the panel may have been painted partly by other painters in the workshop. It is believed to have been painted between 1445 and 1450. Lit.: Salmi p. 75ff.

MELOZZO DA FORLI. 1438-1494.

Born in Forli. We know nothing of his years of apprenticeship. From 1476 until his death in Rome.

ANGEL MUSICIAN (No. 2843). Fresco 0.63 × 0.52 m. Bequeathed to the Museum in 1941 by F. Cambó. The figure resembles in all respects, theme and expression (and no doubt was inspired by) the angel musician from the church of the Holy Apostles in Rome, which is now in the Vatican. However, we discern a disparity in quality compared to the monumentality and the size of the Vatican painting.

MASTER FROM NORTHERN ITALY. About 1480.

ECCE HOMO (No. 580). Wooden panel 0.78 × 0.53 m.

This anonymous master must have known Giacopo Bellini's drawings, as his architecture is very close to the models in Bellini's book of drawings (in Paris). However, the style of the figures and the composition show no resemblance to Bellini. The painting may have been made almost anywhere in northern Italy.

ANTONIAZZO ROMANO. Active 1460-1508.

Umbrian school. He was among the group of followers of B. Gozzoli's workshop. Melozzo da Forli, Perugino, and Ghirlandaio influenced him.

THE VIRGIN WITH THE CHILD (No. 577). Fresco 1.30 × 1.10 m. Both this work and the following probably come from the Spanish church in Rome, S. Giacomo degli Spagnoli.

BOTTICELLI, ALESSANDRO FILIPEPI. 1444-1510.

Born in Florence and worked there all his life except for a stay in Rome in 1482-83. Apprenticed to Fra Filippo Lippi. Lit.: S. Bettini, "Botticelli", Bergamo, 1947.

SCENES FROM THE HISTORY OF NASTAGIO DEGLI HONESTI (Nos. 2838, 2839, 2840). The story is taken from Boccaccio's Decameron, Fifth day, 8th story.

SCENE I (No. 2838). Wooden panel 1.38 × 0.83 m. When Nastagio has been rejected by his lady, he tries to overcome his grief by retiring with his friends to the loneliness of Chiassi near Ravenna. In a pine forest he sees a naked woman attacked by a dog while a knight on horseback throws himself over her with raised sword. Nastagio tries inmediately to help the lady.

SCENE II (No. 2838). Wooden panel 1.38 × 0.82 m.

In the same place the horrified Nastagio sees the body of the dead woman. Her persecutor has wrenched out her heart and entrails and thrown them to the dogs.

SCENE III (No. 2840). Wooden panel 1.42 × 0.84.

Nastagio learns the story which the knight tells him of how this persecution and death are repeated endlessly because of the woman's lack of feeling. Nastagio decides that this punishment should be inflicted on his own unfeeling lady. His friends invite the Traversari family to a banquet in Chiassi. Before the eyes of everyone scene I is repeated. The end of the story is told in another painting which is in the Vernon Watney collection in London. There we see how Nastagio finds kindness in the young Traversari girl, and how she slips away from the banquet that is laid on an open porch. It has been discussed at length whether Botticelli painted these scenes. Most researchers believe that, apart from the London panel, the paintings were made in Botticelli's Florentine workshop. That much appears certain. On the other hand, a study of these scenes cannot fail to reveal that the sketches must have come from the master's hand. (Lit.: S. Bettini, p. 34).

ANDREA MANTEGNA. 1431-1506.

Worked in Padua and Venice and after 1459 in Mantua. Trained in the workshop of F. Squarcione. However, the Florentine painters Donatello, P. Uccello, A. Castagno, and Fra F. Lippi influenced him decisively. Apart from short stays in Florence and Rome, until his death in the service of the Gonzagas in Mantua. Lit.: G. Fiocco, "Mantegna", Milan, 1937; E. Tietze-Conrat, "Mantegna", London, 1955.

THE DEATH OF THE VIRGIN (No. 248). Wooden panel 0.44 × 0,42 m. Acquired for Philip IV from Charles I of England's collection. The fascinating impression of monumental shaping in this composition originals from the precise observation of reality and from the dignified funeral ceremony as well as from the harrowing expression on the faces of the simple apostles. The Mantua landscape increases the mournful tone. The composition included above this painting a Christ in mandorla with the soul of the Virgin. That fragment is in the Vendeghini collection in Ferrara. The painting was done between 1461-63.

ANTONELLO DA MESSINA. About 1430-1479.

Born in Messina. Working in Naples, Reggio (Calabria), and, in 1475-76, in Venice, where he exerted a decisive influence. Apart from that in Messina until his death. Lit.: S. Bottari, *"Antonello"*, Milan-Messina, 1953; X. Salas in *"Gazette des Beaux-Arts"*, 1967, LXX, p. 125f.; L. Sciasca-G. Mandel, *"Antonello da M."*, Milan 1967.

THE DEAD CHRIST SUPPORTED BY AN ANGEL (No. 3092). Panel 0.74 × 0.51 m.

This splendidly preserved work shows Antonello in every respect as a painter of genius: in the grandiose presentation of the composition; in the perfection of the figures and the landscape with its depiction of his native city in the background; and in the profound, harrowing, and passionate expression of the figures. The colours are of the most excellent tones. The painting must have been made between 1475 and 1479. Lit.: X. Salas, 1967, p. 125f.

GIOVANNI BELLINI. 1429(?)-1516.

Born in Venice, son of the painter Jacopo Bellini and brother of Gentile B. He began painting in his father's workshop, influenced by A. Mantegna. Later influenced by Piero della Francesca and Antonello da Messina. Leading Venetian painter before Titian. Lit.: L. Dussler, "*Giovanni Bellini*", Vienna, 1949; R. Palluchini, "Giovanni Bellini", Milan 1959.

THE VIRGIN WITH THE CHILD BETWEEN ST. CATHERINE AND ST. URSULA (No. 50).
Signed: Joannes Bellinus, P. Wooden panel 0.77 × 1.04 m. In 1746 in Philip V's collection in La Granja.

The composition is a variation of a panel that is in the Accademia of Venice (613). Probably done about 1495. Lit.: L. Dussler, p. 92, No. 71; R. Palluchini, p. 140, illust. 152.

ITALIAN PAINTING IN THE 16TH CENTURY: CENTRAL AND NORTHERN ITALY

L. DUSSLER.

While the Tuscan and Umbrian schools of the 15thC are scantily represented in the Prado, the collection of Florentine and Roman paintings from the great classical century that the visitor can admire in the Prado is magnificent. As always, Raphael is clearly the principal painter.

Two first-trate paintings from the 1510 decade represent Raphael as the portrait painter of genius (with the "Cardinal") and the master of the *Sacra Conversazione* (with the "Madonna Pesce"). Following immediately after these are his "Holy families", the biblical stories of the "Visitation" and "Jesus Carrying the Cross" from Raphael's last years. In these paintings we see clearly the imprint of Raphael's personal creation, even though the final execution has depended on his workshop painters.

In the same years Florence gave its contribution to classicism in the person of Andrea del Sarto, whose figures and religious paintings are always of extraordinary quality.

This stylistic period is represented in northern Italy by B. Luini and A. Correggio, painters who were highly regarded in their own times. The latter's two works in the Prado, each a gem within the artist's production, represent the master with the highest honours. No less brilliant is the presence of one of the most typical mannerists, G. F. Parmigianino. His portraits may without hesitating be compared to those in Naples and Vienna.

Sebastino del Piombo, who was Venetian but moved to Rome, followed the same direction. His "Scene in Limbo" and still more "Jesus Carrying the Cross" presage the Spanish concept to such an extent that they duely reserve their place in the Prado.

SARTO, ANDREA D'AGNOLO, CALLED A. DEL SARTO. 1486-1530.

Sarto was a Florentine painter apprenticed to Piero di Cosimo. He was under the influence of Fra Bartolomeo, Leonardo da Vinci, and Raphael. In 1518-19 he was at the court in Paris. Lit.: R. Monti, *"A. del Sarto"*, Milan 1965.

PORTRAIT OF A LADY (No. 322). Wooden panel 0.73 × 0.56 m. In the 18thC the painting was in the Alcázar.

Judging by the structure and expression of the figure, it must have been painted recalling the stamp which Raphael placed on his creations. As the woman's features are repeated several times in Sarto's production, about and after 1515, we may assume that she was his wife, Lucrezia di Baccio del Fede.

SARTO. 1486-1530.

MADONNA DELLA SCALA (No. 334). Wooden panel 1.77 × 1.35 m. The painting is signed on the rug with a monogram. It was acquired for Philip IV from the collection of Charles I of England. In 1657 it was in the Escorial.

The work cited by Vasari (ed. M. V., p. 37f) gets its name because the Virgin Mary is seated on the last step of the stairs. The angel with be book turned towards the child is Tobias. The identification of the companion figure is uncertain. However, as he holds a feather in his hand, he is probably an evangelist; we lack a clearer attribute. Because of the tectonic arrangement, the organic composition, and the spatial distribution of the landscape, the painting is probably a work from Sarto's later years, 1522-23.

RAPHAEL SANZIO. 1483-1520.

Raphael was born in Urbino. He was apprenticed to his father Giovanni S. and particularly to Perugino. From 1504 to 1508 he was in Florence. He was decisively influenced by Fra Bartolomeo and Leonardo da Vinci. From 1508 until his death he lived in Rome. He was inspired to some extent by Michelangelo. Lit.: L. Dussler, *"Raphael, a Critical Catalog"*, London, 1971; J. Pope-Hennessy, *"Raphael"*, London, 1971.

PORTRAIT OF A CARDINAL (No. 299). Wooden panel 0.79 × 0.61 m. In 1818 the painting was in Aranjuez.

To the distinguished and reserved portraits of renaissance prelates is added a form of aristocracy that depends equally on the technical quality of the painting and on the clear lines of the drawing. The intensity of the colours increases the dignified expression. Lit.: L. Dussler Cat, p. 30.

RAPHAEL, 1483-1520.

THE HOLY FAMILY OF THE OAKTREE, CALLED "LA QUERCIA" (No. 303). Wooden panel 1.44 × 1.10 m. Signed on the cradle: Raphael Pinx. In the 18thC in the Palace in Madrid.

The composition is based on a Raphael sketch while the painting was probably done by G. Romano. Raphael used his own recollections for the archaeological fragments. Lit.: L. Dussler Cat, p. 107; J. Pope-Hennesy, p. 221.

RAPHAEL. 1483-1520.

MADONNA DEL PESCE (No. 297). Wooden panel transferred to canvas 2.15 × × 1.58 m. Present to Philip IV from the duke of Medina de las Torres. In 1645 in the Escorial.

The "Madonna pesce" is a prime example of the "miraculous paintings" (Gnadenbilder) from Raphael's mature period. Thanks to its composition of monumental structure, it is a closed unit that shows a majestic ideal type. Lit.: Dussler Cat, p. 38; J. Pope-Hennessy, p. 217f.

RAPHAEL. 1483-1520.

JESUS FALLING ON HIS WAY TO CALVARY (No. 298). Woden panel transferred to canvas 3.18 × 2.29 m. Signed on the stone in the foreground: RAPHAEL URBINAS. In 1663 in Philip IV's collection.

Painted about 1516, probably influenced by Dürer's "small passion" wood-cut with the same theme. It has unjustly been attributed to the workshop assistants. They may have helped with the painting, but the idea belongs to Raphael. He himself has also painted the main figure and the surrounding figures which are full of strong expression. Lit.: L. Dussler Cat, p. 44; J. Pope-Hennessy, p. 27.

RAPHAEL. 1483-1520.

THE VISITATION (No. 300). Wooden panel transferred to canvas 2.00 × 1.45 m. Signed in the lower left corner: Raphael Urbinas F.

The inscription at the center bottom, Marinus Branconius F. F., is the person who commissioned the painting for S. Silvestro in Aquila in 1520. Although it is a workshop painting, that is to say by F. Penni, the design for the painting must have come without any doubt from the master himself. Lit.: L. dussler Cat. p. 52; J. Pope-Hennessy, p. 221.

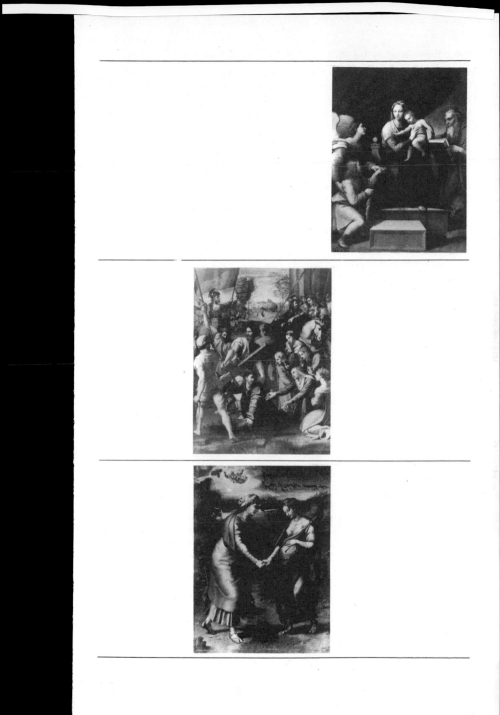

SEBASTIANO LUCIANI, "SEBASTIANO DEL PIOMBO". About 1485-1547.
Born in Venice. From 1511 until his death in Rome. Apprentice of G. Bellini
and worked in Giorgione's workshop. Raphael and particularly Michelangelo
influenced him. Lit.: L. Dussler, "S. del Piompo", Basel, 1942; R. Pallucchini,
"S. Viniziano", Milan, 1944.

CHRIST CARRYING THE CROSS (No. 345). Canvas 1.21 × 1.00 m. In 1656 in the
Escorial in the collection of Philip IV. Painted about 1530.

Sebastiano did the same subject without the accompanying figures and the
background landscape on the right some years later for Charles V's envoy,
Fernando Silva. Now in the Hermitage Museum in Leningrad. Compared to
this picture and the still later one in Budapest, both of which have magnificent
expressive strength, the Prado copy has a soft Venetian reminiscence in
expressión as well as warmer colours. Lit.: L. Dussler Cat, p. 74, 135.

SEBASTIANO DEL PIOMBO. About 1485-1547.

CHRIST IN LIMBO (No. 346). Canvas 2.26 × 1.14 m. Velázquez brought this
painting to the Escorial.

Through a simple and unencumbered composition without any adornment,
the event gains in intense expressive force. That is later seen again in Spanish
painters like F. Ribalta (Valencia, Museum) and others. Sebastiano based his
Christ figure on a drawing by Michelangelo. Lit.: L. Dussler, p. 76, 136.

PERUZZI, BALDASSARE. 1481-1536.

Born in Siena, as a painter and architect mainly in Rome. Lit.: Ch. L. Frommel, *"Peruzzi als Maler und Zeichner"*, Vienna, 1968.

THE RAPE OF THE SABINES (No. 524). Wooden panel 0.47 × 1.57 m.

THE CONTINENCE OF SCIPIO (No. 525). Wooden panel 0.46 × 1.57 m.

The two panels come from a cassone. Their attribution to Peruzzi is as hard to defend as the new suggestion in favour of A. Aspertini. The figures and landscape show a familiarity with the Umbrian and Sienese character of the painter Pinturicchio, are, however, not painted by him.

CORREGGIO, ANTONIO ALLEGRI. About 1489-1534.

Born in Correggio, worked there and in Parma where he painted his main frescos. He died in Correggio. His close masters, Francia and Costa, furthermore Mantegna, Leonardo and the Roman school (Raphael and Michelangelo) influenced him decisively. Lit.: G. Gronau, *"Correggio"*, Stuttgart, 1907.

NOLI ME TANGERE (No. 111). Wooden panel transferred to canvas 1.30 × 1.03 m. The painting was a present to Philip IV from the duke of Medina de las Torres. It was in the Escorial in 1667.

Painted in 1523-25 and mentioned already by Vasari (ed. M. IV, p. 116) when it was in Bologna. No other painter has expressed with so much feeling the loneliness of the scene of the meeting between the risen Christ and the repentant woman in a magnificent mountain landscape. Here the Magdalen's exalted look at the Master verges on the border of feminine hysteria. The palette helps to increase the tone of the expression. Lit.: G. Gronau, p. 90.

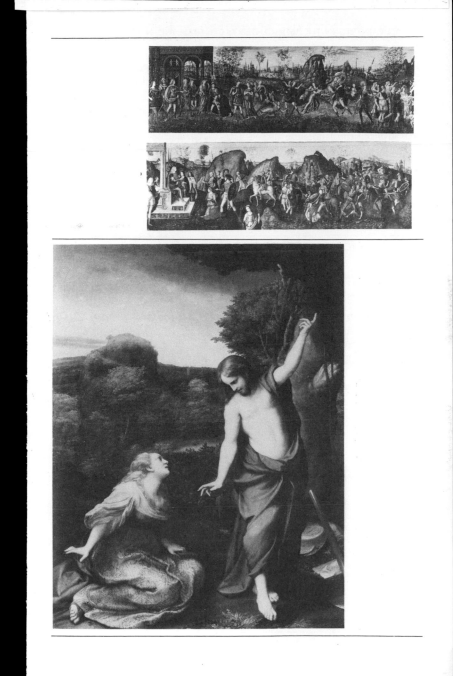

CORREGGIO. About 1489-1534.

THE VIRGIN WITH THE CHILD AND ST. JOHN (No. 112). Wooden panel 0.48 × 0.37 m. In Isabel de Farnesio's collection. In 1746 in La Granja.

The small panel belongs to the painter's most proliferate period, about 1515. It captivates as much by the idyllic childlike quality of the mother playing with the two children as by the loneliness of the landscape. Leonardo da Vinci may have inspired the landscape theme. Lit.: G. Gronau, p. 21.

PARMIGIANINO, FRANCESCO MAZZOLA. 1503-1540.

Apprenticed to his two uncles P. J. and M. Mazzola in Parma, influenced by A. Correggio. In Rome in 1524-27 he was inspired by Raphael and Michelangelo. In Bologna in 1527-31 and after that in Parma. Lit.: P. J. Freedberg, *"Parmigianino"*, Cambridge, 1950.

PORTRAIT OF PIETRO MARIA ROSSI, COUNT OF S. SECONDO (No. 279). Canvas 1.33 × 0.98 m. In 1686 in the Escorial.

Painted about 1535 it counts as one of the master's best portraits, forming a pair with the following portrait of the lady with the children. The figure shows magnificent composition and characterizes accurately the aristocratic pose and expression. The composition is effectively highlighted by the small bronze statue. The background shows a landscape with architecture. The overall pictorial theme is magnificent.

16TH CENTURY PAINTING IN VENICE

L. DUSSLER.

The Prado Museum owes its fame mainly to the Spanish masters from the "Golden Century" and to its unique collection of Titians which here, as nowhere else, goes back to the painter's royal clients, Charles V and Philip II.

Titian's paintings lead us back in the times of those kings and to the fame and glory of their power. They bring the master before our eyes in all his individual sensitivity. Nevertheless, the visitor will not fail to be accurately informed about the royal art lovers' personal taste as well as about their aims as collectors of paintings, whether of religious or profane subjects.

Since the interests of the sovereigns as collectors were ambitious, Titian had the opportunity to exhibit his unique mastery and universal knowledge in carrying out the tasks required to fulfill the royal desires.

Philip IV kept the memory of his ancestors' plan and followed, as if it were an order, the example of his elders. It is thanks to him that the Prado today along with middle and late period works can exhibit such brilliant paintings from Titian's first period as "The Offering to the Goddess of Love" and "The Bacchanal". Thus the great master's beginning - zenith - old age can be followed in the Prado through paintings of the highest quality.

Actually the beginning of this collection goes back to the times of his great master Giorgione whose "Sacra Conversazione" makes clear their common points and differences of tone.

The young coryphaeus J. Jacopo Tintoretto, in whose creations El Greco was so interested, was also the object of interest by the collectors as we can see in the acquisitions from Philip IV's time. There are several good examples of his paintings in the Prado, particularly the masterly "Gentleman with the Gold Chain". However, his Old Testament scenes are more important with their inventive arrangement, and the magic of their composition. Velázquez himself acquired these "Poesie" during his stay in Venice.

In the same century a shipment of P. Veroneses arrived in Spain. Among them were some as excellent as "Christ and the Centurion" and "The Finding of Moses".

The interesting figure of Lotto should not be overlooked. His art as a portrait painter, which was supreme all during his life, is brought out in the fine "Portrait of the Betrothed", "The Downhill Slope of Life", and "St. Jerome in Penitence".

The historical paintings from the Old and the New Testament by the Bassano family show that the royal collectors understood what these artists had to offer. Among these paintings the "Scene of Paradise" (No. 21), which Philip IV received as a present from the duke of Savoy, plays an important role.

GIORGIONE (GIORGIO DA CASTELFRANCO). About 1477-1510.
Apprenticed to Giovanni Bellini, active en Venice. Lit.: Justi, "Giorgione" (2. edition), Berlin, 1926; G. M. Richter, "Giorgio da Castelfranco", Chicago, 1937; L. Baldass-G. Heinz, "Giorgione", Vienna, 1964.

THE VIRGIN ON THE THRONE WITH THE CHILD, ST. ANTHONY OF PADUA AND ST. ROCK (No. 288). Canvas 0.92 × 1.33 m. A present from the duke of Medina de las Torres to Philip IV. In 1657 in the Escorial.

It is attributable either to Giorgione or to the young Titian. However, the method in which it is painted, the interpretation, and the intimate and lyrical expression definitely speak in favor of Giorgione. The unfinished painting is among his last works.

VICENZO CATENA. About 1480-1531.
Vicenzo was a Venetian painter, influenced by Giovanni Bellini and partly by Giorgione. Active in Venice. Lit.: G. Robertson, "V. Catena", Edinburg, 1954.

JESUS GIVING THE KEYS TO PETER (No. 20). Wooden panel 0.86 × 1.35 m. Came to the Prado from the Escorial.

The fine and well balanced composition is alluring mainly because of the group of three feminine figures, whose virtues are finely individualized. There is a slightly later version in the Gardner Museum in Boston which is set under an open sky. The Prado painting was probably made about 1517. Lit.: G. Robertson, No. 31, p. 56.

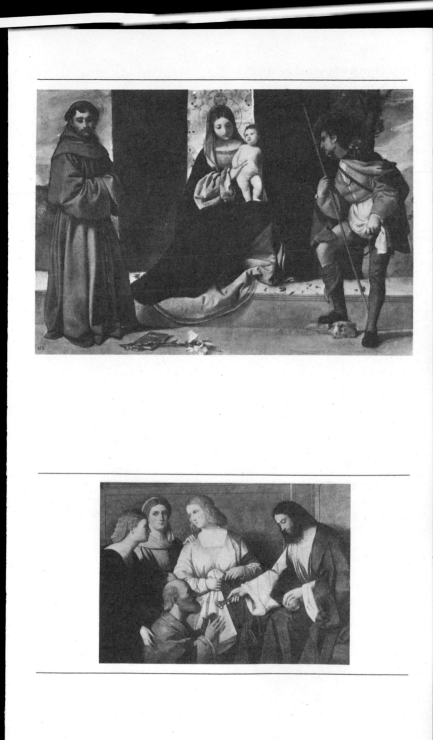

LORENZO LOTTO. 1480-1556.

Lotto was a Venetian apprenticed to Alvise Vivarini. Influenced by Giovanni Bellini. Active in Venice, Rome, the Lombardy, and in the Marches, where he spent his last years in Loretto. Lit.: B. Berenson, *"L. Lotto"*, Milan, 1955.

PORTRAIT OF MARSILIO WITH HIS FIANCEE (No. 240). Wooden panel 0.71 × 0.84 m. Signed and dated next to Cupid's hand: Lotus Pictor 1523. Quoted by Anonimo Morelliano (ed. Frizzoni, p. 140) as being in the house of Z. Cassoto in Bergamo. In 1666 in the Alcázar in Madrid.

The marvellously painted portrait combines excellent characterization of the persons with the impressive carrying out of the elegant costumes and the very particular psychological accentuation of the situation, the heightening of which has been attributed to the smiling cupid holding the yoke over the couple. Berenson, p. 82.

LORENZO LOTTO. 1480-1556.

ST. JEROME (No. 448). Wooden panel 0.99 × 0.90 m. In his account books from 1544 and 1546, Lotto cites "St. Jerome in Penitence". There is another version of this in the Galleria Doria in Rome. The painting was brought to the Escorial in 1593.

The representation reveals the introversion dominating Lotto's late phase, together with a summary tendency; quite the opposite of the same topic of 1506 in the Louvre. The hovering angel carries a plate with the inscription: Nunc legit nunc oral nunc perfore crimina plorat. Lit.: Bereson, p. 70.

TITIAN, VECELLIO. 1487/90-1576.
Born in Pieve di Cadore. In Gentile and Giovanni Bellini's workshop, worked jointly with Giorgione. Active in Venice, Padua, Bologna, Augsburg, and Rome. Court painter for Charles V and Philip II. He died in Venice. Lit.: E. Panofsky, "Problems in Titian", London, 1969; H. Wethey, "Titian, I. The Religious Paintings", London, 1969; II, "The Portraits", London, 1971; III, "The Mythological and Historical Paintings", London, 1975; Pallucchini, Tiziano, Florence, 1969.

THE VIRGIN AND THE CHILD, ST. DOROTHY AND ST. GEORGE (No. 434). Wooden panel 0.86 × 1.30 m. 1593 in the Escorial.

This delicate "Sacra Conversazione" was formerly attributed to Giorgione. Later it has been dated to Titian's early period about 1506, and it has even occasionally been doubted whether it was a Titian at all. It is, however, without any doubt an authentic work by Titan from about 1515. The madonna's head is similar to that of Venus in the painting in villa Borghese in Rome. St. George is very close to St. Rock in the altar of San Marco in Santa María della Salute in Venice. Dorothy is related to the type of woman that appears in "The Miracle of St. Anthony" in the Scuola del Santo de Padua. Lit.: Wethey I, No. 65; Pallucchini, p. 249.

TITIAN. 1487/90-1576.

THE OFFERING TO THE GODDESS OF LOVE (No. 419). Canvas 1.72 × 1.75 m. See No. 418, below.

TITIAN. 1487/90-1576.

BACCHANAL (No. 418). Canvas 1.75 × 1.93 m.

The painting is connected with G. Bellini's "Feast of the Gods" (National Gallery, Washington) finished by Titian after Bellini's death in 1516. It was meant for the library in duke Alfonso d'Este's Ferrara palace. The master was commissioned to make two mythological paintings for the same room. The descriptions are recorded in the Imagines VI by the ancient writer Filostrato. A) The feast of Venus. B) The Bacchanal or the Inhabitants of the Isle of Andros. Even though the paintings have as their source the abovementioned narrative, they are still dominated by so much inventive and admirable poetic fantasy that not the least trace of literary background is seen in them. The richness of the figures in motion, the infantile ingenuousness of the postures, the captivating vitality that appears in the offering to the goddess of love, the fusion of the group that is thrown onto nature's stage, and the combination of colour and light are unsurpassed in the history of painting. The Bacchanal: the scene presents the turbulance of the basic joy of men and women in the figures of bacchi and Venus' maidens. Whether they are naked or dressed, lying or standing couples and single figures, Titian always manages to make of them rhythmic groups with a triumphant general effect. There is an inseparable alliance between the phenomenon of nature and the masterly orchestration of colours on the one hand, and on the other the intensity of the moving groups. The baroque rediscovered life and beauty in the composition as is demonstrated by the Rubens copy in Stockholm and the Van Dyck copy in Gothenburg. Lit.: Wethey III, No. 13.

TITIAN. 1487/90-1576.
PORTRAIT OF CHARLES V WITH HIS DOG (No. 409). Canvas 1.92 × 1.11 m. In 1666 in the Alcázar.
This portrait which depicts the monarch together with his dog was painted while the Emperor stayed in Bologna (from november 1532 until the end of february 1533). A portrait, likewise made in Bologna, by the Austrian court painter Jacob Seisenegger (1505-1567) served as model for this painting, undoubtedly after the Emperor's own wish. The Seisenegger portrait is now in the Kunsthistorische Museum in Vienna. By his genius, however, Titian created a portrait which, without changing the pose or the magnificent dress, leaves Seisenegger's work far behind. Titian's portrait is a masterful interpretation with an appealing harmony of colours and a vigourous suppression of details. The difference in this concept is even seen in the way the dog poses with the Emperor. Lit.: Wethey II, No. 20; Panofsky, p. 182ff; Pallucchini, p. 208f.

TITIAN. 1487/90-1576.

FEDERIGO GONZAGA II (No. 408). Wooden panel 1.25 × 0.99 m. Signed: Titianus F. In 1666 in the Alcázar.

In the early 1520's Titian became acquainted with the house of Gonzaga in Mantua. This contact with the great art-loving duke was maintained henceforth. The portrait of Federigo was finished about 1525. It shows how Titian's control of composition and colour already at this early date enabled him to portray princely nobility. Splendour and discretion govern the rendition, as we see in the precision of the dark blue silk cloth of the jacket and in the red band of sash with its delicate, scarlet stretch, as well as in the hair and the beard. Even the animal's intricate hair is masterfully painted. Lit.: Pallucchini, p. 261; Wethey II, No. 49.

TITIAN. 1487/90-1576.

PORTRAIT OF PHILIP II (No. 411). Canvas 1.93 × 1.11 m. In 1600 in the Alcázar. The portrait shows Philip II full-length at the age of 23. It was painted in Augsburg between the end of 1550 and May of 1551 and recalls Titian's portrait of Charles V (1532-33). Here the Emperor's dignity was accentuated without any attention to the background. In the painting of Charles V's successor, on the other hand, it is not only the room with the red carnation on the table that is important, but also a decisive preponderance in the beautiful and shining cuirass with its golden-verdant flashes, a masterpiece from the Agusburg armourer. The young sovereign stands as if preparing to review the troops. The portrait of Charles V on horseback makes it possible to perceive what heights Titian's brush could reach. This portrait of Philip II is the equal to that of Charles V. Lit.: Wethey II, No. 78; Pallucchini, No. 369.

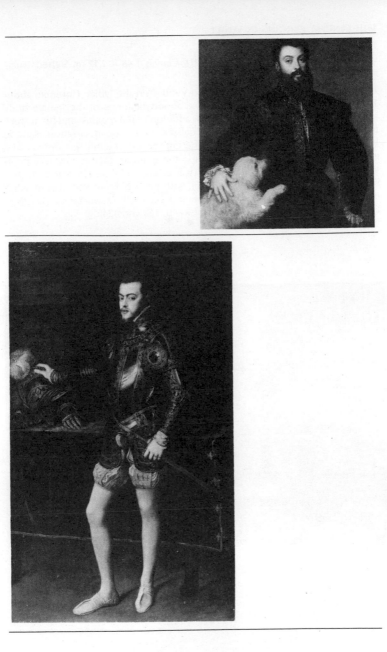

TITIAN. 1487/90-1576.

VENUS, CUPID, AND ORGANIST (No. 421). Canvas 1.48 × 2.17 m. Signed: Titianus F. In 1636 in the Alcázar.

The contrast to the so-called "Urbino Venus" (in the Uffizi, Florence, about 1538) is obvious in this version by the abundant forms of the female body and the lack of decorum as well as the addition of the organist and his gesture towards Venus. Since both are individualized there is no idealization as in the Urbino Venus, and one gets rather the impression of a mistress instead of a goddess. It is almost certain that this is the painting that in 1548 belonged to bishop Granvella and which in 1600 was given to Philip III by Rudolf II. The Prado's other Venus version (No. 420), without cupid and with a somewhat older organist, must be a little later and be partly a workshop painting. Lit.: Pallucchini, p. 290 and 293; Panofsky, p. 122 and 124f.

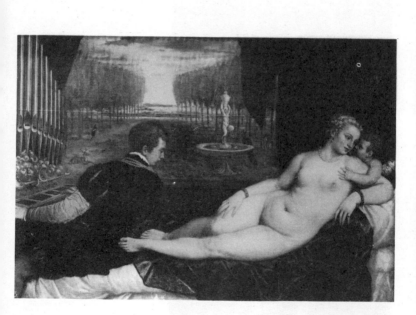

TITIAN. 1487/90-1576.

VENUS AND ADONIS (No. 422). Canvas 1.86 × 2.07 m. In 1636 in the Alcázar.

It belongs to a cycle commissioned to Titian during Philip II's stay in Augsburg from the end of 1550 to August 1551. It was to consist of eight scenes arranged in pairs and destined for the King's apartments. The present painting and Danae (see No. 425) were the first. The painter announced their finishing in 1553. The tight, friezelike composition shows the melodic rhythm of the group. The movement is slipping away towards the group of hunting dogs and the landscape. Antique motifs (Venus) are combined with the freshness of nature. It is all crowned by a warm palette which is marvellous "in this poesy" which already Titian's contemporary L. Dolce had extolled. Lit.: Panofsky, p. 150f; Pallucchini, p. 299.

TITIAN. 1487/90-1576.

DANAE (No. 425). Canvas 1.29 × 1.80 m. Like No. 422 commissioned to Titian by Philip II. This poetic version of a classic subject was meant by Titian himself to form a pair with No. 422.

The reclining frontal figure offsets the figure seen from behind in the "Venus and Adonis" painting. While No. 422 is a first version, Titian is in "Danae" dealing with a subject he had worked with before, in 1545 (National Museum in Naples). However, this is a new edition. It not only includes the avaricious servant who in her apron catches Jupiter's golden rain, which adds a dynamic quality to the scene that is absent in the Naples painting, but the figure of Danae herself and her surroundings have been varied in the finest shades. Only the original painting can bring to the fore to what degree the interpretation and the fortunate palette partake in this version. Lit.: Panofsky, p. 149f; Pallucchini, p. 300.

TITIAN. 1487/90-1576.

SALOME (No. 428). Canvas 0.87 × 0.80 m. In 1666 in the Alcázar.

The model for this young woman is commonly accepted to have been Titian's daughter Lavinia. Already in 1555 he had painted her in the same pose carrying a silver fruitdish. That painting is now in Berlin. Although this picture suffered somewhat in the Alcázar fire, Titian's elegant and light interpretation is still discernible in the incarnate, the head-dress and in the brilliant red colour of the dramask dress, both of which are typical of his style in the 1560's. Lit.: Wethey I, No. 141; Pallucchini, p. 484.

TITIAN. 1487/90-1576.

EQUESTRIAN PORTRAIT OF CHARLES V (No. 410). Canvas 3.32 × 2.79 m. In 1600 the portrait was in the treasury building, in 1614 in El Pardo.

The portrait of the Emperor on horseback, the most important equestrian painting in European painting, immortalizes Charles V after the battle of Mühlberg in 1547. The sovereign was then at the height of his power. Although the Emperor, his armour, and horse are related to reality, and the landscape, unknown to Titian, refers to the Elbe landscape, this painting is not a historical account but the monument of a defender of faith. The monumentality is stressed both by the monarch's solitude and by his firm expression. His character of "God-sent" is sustained. Only when seeing the original can the spectator appreciate to what unusual degree Titian's mastery elevated this figure with its armour, its sash, and its horse-trappings, lifted the open sky and the oncoming night, not to mention the looks of the Emperor, to the marvellous and grandiose whole that is this portrait. Lit.: Wethey II, No. 21; Panofsky; Pallucchini, p. 289.

TITIAN. 1487/90-1576.

LATE SELF PORTRAIT (No. 407). Canvas 0.86 × 0.65 m. The painting was acquired during the reign of Philip IV. In 1666 it was in the Alcázar.

This very late portrait from about 1570 of the almost nonegenarian sovereign of painters does not in its features contradict the traces of old age. However, because Titian chose to portray himself in profile, the features are marked as in a relief with clear cut lines. There is nothing superfluous about the portrait; one does not even perceive the colours directly. All the more penetrating is the strength of the gaze that now embraces the sum of all that has been attained. Lit.: Wethey II, No. 105; Pallucchini, p. 323.

TITIAN. 1487/90-1576.

SPAIN COMES TO THE AID OF RELIGION (No. 430). Canvas 1.68 × 1.68 m. Signed on the stone in the lower right hand corner: Titianus F. In 1600 in the Alcázar.

Originally the composition was intended as a mythological scene for Alfonso d'Este I of Ferrara, and as such G. Vasari (ed. M. VII, p. 458) saw it in Titian's workshop in 1566. After the battle of Lepanto (1571) Titian changed it to an allegorical scene, which soon after it was finished in 1574 went to Philip II's collection. The contrast between Religion in a humble gesture, threatened from behind by the nest of serpents of heresy and from the sea by Turkish ships, and the triumphant heroine representing Spain is underlined by a rich coloristic orchestration coresponding in its powerful expressive execution to Titian's late style. Lit.: Wethey I, No. 88; Panofsky, p. 186f; Pallucchini, p. 327.

TITIAN. 1487/90-1576.

ADAM AND EVE (No. 429). Canvas 2.40 × 1.86 m. The painting is signed on the stone to the left: TITIANUS F. In 1600 it was in the Alcázar.

Painted about 1570. In spite of the advanced deterioration of the painting it is one of the most penetrating works of Titian's late period. This is due not only to the monumental conception and the magnificent figures, particularly Eve's charming body and seductive gesture, but equally much to the mystery that surrounds the event. Guilt and original sin were hardly ever recalled with such intensity. Rubens was profoundly impressed by the composition (see his version in the Prado, No. 1692), but he did not attain the depth of Titian's interpretation. Lit.: Wethey I, No. 1; Panofsky, p. 27f; Pallucchini, p., 320f.

JACOPO ROBUSTI, CALLED TINTORETTO. 1518-1594.

Active almost exclusively in Venice. Michelangelo and Parmigianino decisively influenced the formation of his style. Lit.: E. von den Bercken, *"Tintoretto"*, Munich, 1942; R. Pallucchini, *"La giovinezza del Tintoretto"*, Milán, 1950.

GENTLEMAN WITH GOLDEN CHAIN (No. 378). Canvas 1.03X0.76m. In 1686 in the Alcázar.

This elegant aristocrat represents Tintoretto's excellence as a portrait painter of the highest quality. It shows his masterly precisión in the overall composition and his concentration on the essential, i.e. the noble head full of expression and the affirmative strength in the gentleman's carriage. The portrait was painted about 1550.

TINTORETTO. 1518-1594.

A PROCURER FROM THE VENETIAN REPUBLIC (No. 379). Canvas 0.77 × 0.63 m.

Dignity and wisdom of old age are combined in the magnificently modelled features of this high official. The portrait was painted about 1580.

VERONESE, PAOLO CALIARI. 1528-1588.

Apprenticed to the Verona painter A. Badile. In 1555 in Venice where he did most of his work. His stay in Rome in 1560 had a definitive influence on his style. Lit.: G. Fiocco, "P. Veronese", 1934.

VENUS AND ADONIS (No. 482). Canvas 2.12 × 1.91 m. In 1686 in the Alcázar.

It was bought by Velázquez in Venice for the Court. Compared to Titian's elegant and rhythmic painting of the same subject, Veronese's composition is dense. However, in all its decorative details it does not lack the charm of sensual fascination and the spell of nature. It was painted about 1580.

VERONESE. 1528-1588.

JESUS AND THE CENTURION (No. 492). Canvas 1.92 × 2.97 m. Philip IV acquired the painting at Charles I of England's assets. In 1657 it was in the Escorial.

The painting is based on a story in Matthew, 8, in which the centurion from Capernaum begs the Lord on his knees to cure his servant. It belongs to the series of paintings with historic scenes of ceremonial character, a genre of which Veronese was an unsurpassed master. It does not matter whether he dealt with scenes from the Old and New Testament or with profane events. In the present painting, which is composed like a frieze against an architectural background, the group begging for grace in a marvellously rhythmic series contrasts with the group that grants the grace. Here the artist found a convincing expression of noble and fine humanity. The Prado painting, from the painter's mature age (about 1570), must be counted amongst his most impressive works. Lit.: G. Fiocco, p. 201.

VERONESE. 1528-1588.

MOSES SAVED FROM THE WATERS (No. 502). Canvas 0.50 × 0.43 m. In 1666 in the Alcázar.

The friezelike arrangement in Tintoretto's "Moses Being Rescued From the Nile" (No. 396) finds in Veronese's composition of reduced size an authentic monumental configuration. This is not only obvious in the felicitous, beautiful and articulated group of figures, but also in the inclusion of nature - the clear sky and the two well-balanced trees. The view of the city in the middle background to the left with the arch of the bridge increases the opulent beauty of the painting. The subject serves the painter as a means to develop his inclination towards the decorative. We can admire this tendency in the princess' beautiful dress as well as in the care with the other persons are done. The painter's wish to repeat the work is understandable in view of the jubilant orchestration his palette has attained here. None of the replicas (Dresden, Lyon, Washington) has reached the freshness and brilliant effect of the Prado painting which very probably was done about 1570. Lit.: G. Fiocco, p. 201.

VERONESE. 1528-1588.

JESUS IN THE TEMPLE WITH THE DOCTORS (No. 491). Canvas 2.36 x 4.30 m. In the Alcázar in 1686. Dated on the edge of the book held by the person seated at the column to the left: MDXLVIII.

The idea of this large painting clearly reveals Veronese's early style. (A very similar painting by Bassano is in Oxford's Ashmolean Museum.) The audacious architectonic pomp of the temple's interior is organically not dominated, and the group of listeners to the left remains isolated. The young Jesus is painted in a somewhat academic style. One the other hand, in the group to the right there are good solutions to later problems; thus the excellent figures of the oriental and of the jew seated in front of him. Lit.: G. Fiocco, p. 201.

PAINTING IN THE 17TH AND 18TH CENTURY

L. DUSSLER.

It is due to two circumstances that the Prado displays an astonishing great number of Italian baroque masters. The first is Spain's inner ability to accept naturalism which in that country is found documented in the most varied forms, penetrating all aspects of life. On the other hand, there was a great tolerance towards national differences and the wish to employ artists from other countries.

Naturalism's clearest precursor was Ribera, who through his work for decades for the viceroys of Naples created a center which to a certain degree attracted almost all his contemporaries.

Once this school was formed, its effect was more or less lasting, depending on various circumstances. Until after 1700, influences have been active in the metropolis which corresponded with Spanish mentality and therefore were well acepted in Madrid. Thus the oeuvre of M. Stanzione, M. Preti, by the two Gentileschis, A. Vaccaro, Solimena, and B. Cavallino was gathered by their contemporary and future collectors.

Nevertheless, the collecting of paintings with the opposite tendency was not abandoned, that is to say works of the academic Bologna school as represented by magnificent creations by Annibale and Ludovico Caracci, Guercino, Domenichino, and Reni.

M. Preti and Cavarozzi worked in Spain for a short time; L. Giordano and C. Giaquinto were there several years, called by the Court; and G. B. Tiepolo stayed for eight glorius years. His masterful creations in the palaces of Madrid and Aranjuez, his designs and paintings of religious subjects proclaim his fame. Thus, once more, Venice, with the most talented representative of the period, is the city that closes the glorious series of Italian paintings with Titian's art as the shining center.

CARAVAGGIO, MICHELANGELO MERISI. 1573-1610.

Born in Caravaggio in Lombardy, apprenticed to S. Peterzano in Milan. From 1589-1606 active in Rome, temporarily in Naples. 1607-08 in Malta, Syracuse, Messina, and Palermo. Lit.: R. Hinks, "Caravaggio", London, 1953; F. Baumgart, "Caravaggio", Berlin, 1955; W. Friedländer, "Caravaggio Studies", Princeton, 1955; R. Longhi, "Caravaggio", Milan, 1957.

DAVID DEFEATING GOLIATH (No. 65). Canvas 1.10 × 0.91 m. In 1686 in the Alcázar.

There are divided opinions about who painted this canvas. Some researchers like R. Longhi and R. Hinks consider it an original painting from Caravaggio's earliest period, F. Baumgart and W. Friedländer object to it. The bold and yet rather lax composition supports the first theory. Lit.: R. Longhi, p. 25; Baumgart, p. 102; Hinks, p. 104; Friedländer, p. 203.

BORGIANNI, ORAZIO. 1578-1616.

Roman painter influenced by the Bassani and El Greco. In Spain until 1603. Bade in Italy, influenced mainly by Caravaggio's art without succeeding in joining his course.

SELF PORTRAIT (No. 877). Canvas 0.95 × 0.71 m.

With its self-conscious expression and the forceful posture of the person the bravado of this portrait reveals the artist's strong will. Probably done in Rome about 1610.

GUERCINO, FRANCESCO GIOVANNI BARBIERI. 1591-1665.

Born in Cento, educated under B. Schedone, L. Carracci, and the Venetian School. Briefly in Rome, Piacenza, and Modena, after 1642 in Bologna. Lit.: N. Grimaldi, *"Il Guercino"*, Bologna, 1958.

THE LIBERATION OF ST. PETER (No. 200). Canvas 1.05 × 1.36 m. From the marquis of La Ensenada's collection it came to the Royal Palace by 1772.

The painting is an excellent example of Guercino's style in the early 1620's. The figure of St. Peter shows all signs of realism while the Angel in its type and gesture is closer to Bologna classicism. "Matthew and the Angel" and "Saint Petronella's Burial" in the Capitoline Museum in Rome are the Guercinos closest related to this painting.

GUERCINO. 1591-1665.

SUSANNA AND THE TWO OLD MEN (No. 201). Canvas 1.75 × 2.07 m. In 1767 in the Escorial. Painted for cardinal Alessandro Ludovisi in Rome.

This early masterpiece by Guercino was commissioned by cardinal Ludovisi for his private collection along with "Lot and His Daughters" (Escorial) and "The Prodigal Son" (Turin). The paintings are mentioned in a 1617 letter by Ludovico Carracci. Guercino painted the subject several times. In no other composition, however, did he achieve such a tense form. That is amply shown in the woman's voluptuous and luminous body with its beautiful posture, in the realistic figures of the two old men to the left, and in their ardent desire which reaches even to the vibrations of their gestures.

GIORDANO, LUCA. 1632-1705.
Neapolitan, early influenced by Ribera. Intermittently in Venice and Florence. From 1692 to 1702 at the courts of Charles II and Philip V in Madrid. The last years in Naples. Lit.: O. Ferrari-B. Scavizzi, "L. Giordano", Rome, 1966.

LOT AND HIS DAUGHTERS (No. 153). Canvas 0.58 × 1.54 m. The painting belongs to a series of Old Testament scenes in the Royal Palace. Painted 1694-96. Lit.: Ferrari-B. Scavizzi, p. 197.

GIORDANO. 1632-1705.
BETHSHEBA IN THE BATH (No. 165). Canvas 2.19 × 2.12 m. In 1772 in the Palace in Madrid.

Painted about 1700, the canvas served as a model for a tapestry in the Madrid tapestry factory. Lit.: O. Ferrari-B. Scavizzi II, p. 212.

VACCARO, ANDREA. 1598-1670.
Neapolitan painter. After his mannerist education under G. Imparato, he joined the Caravaggio vein through contacts with A. Gentileschi and M. Stanzione, and thus took over Bolognese suggestions. Active in Naples.

REBECCA AND ISAAC AT THE WELL (No. 468). Canvas 1.95 × 2.46 m. Signed: AV. In 1772 in the Royal Palace in Madrid.

The magnificent work with its clear composition belongs to the painter's mature years. The Bologna components assert themselves without any loss of Vaccaro's naturalism.

GIAQUINTO, CORRADO. 1700-1765.

Born in Molfetta, apprenticed to N. M. Rossi and F. Solimena in Naples. After 1723 in Rome where he joined S. Conca to participate in various commissioned works; mainly in Turin. 1753-62 he succeeded Amigoni as court painter in Madrid. There he became director of the Academy of San Fernando. Until his death in Naples.

RISE OF THE SUN AND THE TRIUMPH OF BACCHUS (No. 103). Canvas 1.68 × × 1.40 m. In 1794 in the Retiro.

During his stay in Spain Giaquinto had to execute many commissioned wall and ceiling paintings in the Royal Palace, the Buen Retiro, Aranjuez, and the Escorial. The preliminary studies for some of these are in the Prado; the ingenious trend of Rococo painting is already evident in these sketches.

ROSA, SALVATORE. 1615-1673.

Neapolitan painter and poet, apprenticed to D. A. Greco, F. Fracanzano, influenced by G. Ribera. Active in Rome, Naples, and Florence. After 1649 permanently in Rome. Lit.: Salerno, "S. Rosa", Florence, 1963.

THE GULF OF SALERNO (No. 324). Canvas 1.70 × 2.60 m. Signed: S. R. In 1794 in the Retiro.

Among Rosa's polyfaceted work, his paintings of harbours play an important part. The Pitti Gallery has several. The present one may have been created between 1640 and 1650.

STROZZI, BERNARDO, CALLED "IL CAPPUCCINO". 1581-1644.

Born in Genoa, developed in the circle of Vanni, Salimbeni, and Procaccini. After .1631 in Venice influenced by D. Feti. Lit.: G. Fiocco, "B. Strozzi", Rome, 1921.

VERONICA'S VEIL (No. 354). Canvas 1.68 × 1.18 m. In 1746 in La Granja.

It is from Strozzi's mature period in Genoa. Among the highly qualified master's works, this one holds an important place both because of the composition of its subject and because of the beauty of its colours.

TIEPOLO, GIOVANNI B. 1696-1770.

Born in Venice, apprenticed to Gr. Lazzarini. Strongly influenced by G. B. Piazzatta, Ricci, and P. Veronese, he worked in Venice and the Veneto. 1750-53 in Würzburg, from 1762 until his death in Madrid. Lit.: A. Morassi, "A Complete Catalogue of the Paintings of G. B. Tiepolo", London, 1962.

ANGEL WITH MONSTRANCE (No. 364). Canvas 1.85 × 1.78 m.

The painting was part of the high altar in the church of San Pascual in Aranjuez. The fragment below this painting showing St. Pascual Baylon is also in the Prado (No. 364a). It dates about 1769. Lit.: Morassi, p. 21.

FLEMISH PAINTERS OF THE 17TH CENTURY

W. BRAUNFELS.

The death of the eldest Brueghel in 1569 did not bring about any change in period. P. P. Rubens who would dominate the next period respected Brueghel and learned from him the value of form. However, in 1568, one year before the death of Brueghel, the revolt against the Spanish rule had begun. The Calvinist provinces in the north separated from the Catholic ones in the south.

In 1609 the treaty granting independence to the seven northern provinces was signed. One year earlier Rubens had returned to Antwerp from his Italian journey. The political independence truly marked a new chapter in the history of Flemish painting. The separation meant a change in the cultural situation of both sides. The Flemish in the south came decidedly to represent the Catholic and aristocratic culture of the Baroque. The Dutch in the north just as resolutely expressed Protestant, bourgeois style in their painting and classicism in their architecture.

Philip IV collected works from all the Flemish painters of any interest, that is to say those that at one time or another worked for the governors in Brussels. Among them was first and foremost Rubens, and also Van Dyck, Snyders, and Teniers.

At the beginning of the .18thC Isabel de Farnesio very discerningly perfected this collection. Today it forms the third great and very important group of foreign paintings in the Prado, along with early Flemish painting and Venetian painting from the 16thC.

JAN BRUEGHEL "THE ELDER". 1568-1625.

Second son of the great P. Brueghel "the Elder". 1593-96 in Italy. In 1597 master painter in Antwerp and later, in Brussels, court painter to archduke Albert of Austria. Friend of Rubens'.

JAN BRUEGHEL " THE ELDER". 1568-1625.
THE FIVE SENSES (Nos. 1394-98).

SIGHT (No. 1394). Wooden panel 0.65 × 1.09 m.

HEARING (No. 1395). Wooden panel 0.65 × 1.07 m.

SMELL (No. 1396). Wooden panel 0.65 × 1.09 m. Signed and dated: 1617 and 1618. A present from the duke of Pfalz-Neuburg to the victor from the battle of Nördlingen, cardinal-infante D. Fernando, 1634. (Compare Rubens No. 1687.) From the 16thC until the end of the 18thC the beauty and richness of the world and the joy of love were interpreted in art through allegories of the five senses. Jan Brueghel "the Elder" used his art to unite in one painting precious as well as delicious things. It is always Venus enjoying them. The joys of sight are shown in the works of Fine Arts, among them famous antique pieces and paintings by Rubens. The joys of hearing are illustrated by musical instruments and chimes of clocks. There are also hunting horns. An abundance of flowers brings to memory the olfactory pleasure. A richly layed table with view into the kitchen symbolizes the joy of tasting. Venison, oysters, fish, and all kinds of fruit are combined into a still-life. Vulcan's forge and a whole arsenal of weapons join with paintings of disasters of war and the flagellation of Christ to illustrate the sense of feeling. Saws, rods and braziers belong to the impression of touch, as does Venus' affectionate embrace of Cupid.

W. SAUERLÄNDER.

PETER PAUL RUBENS. 1577-1640.
Rubens is the leading figure of the Flemish School of the 17thC. 1599-1608 he
was in Italy as court painter to the duke of Mantua. In 1603 he visited Spain for
the first time. After 1609 he was in Antwerp where, as head of a large
workshop, he worked for the Church and the courts of Europe. His creative
work covers a full repertory: Altars, epitaphs, mythological and historical
subjects, landscapes and hunting scenes. He designed tapestries and book
frontispieces. He personally oversaw the distribution of his engraved works.
Rubens had received a thorough classical education.
He corresponded with the foremost antiquaries of his time and possessed a
significant collection of art works. He was court painter to the Spanish regents
in Brussels. The infanta Isabel Clara made him her confidant; between 1628
and 1630 he was entrusted with diplomatic missions at the courts of Madrid
and London. Lit.: Roger Avermaete, *"Rubens and His Times"*, London, 1968;
Jakob Burckhardt, *"Erinnerungen aus Rubens"*, Leipzig, 1928; *"Corpus
Rubenianum Ludwig Burchard I"*, Brussels, 1972; H. Vlieghe, Saints, *"Corpus
Rubenianum Ludwig Burchard IX"*, Brussels, 1971; S. Alpers, *"The Decoration
of the Torre de la Parada"*; Hans Gerhard Evers, *"Rubens und sein Werk"*,
Brussels, 1943; Julius S. Held, *"Peter Paul Rubens"*, London, 1954; Rudolf
Oldenbourg, *"P. P. Rubens = Klassiker der Kunst"*, vol. 5, Stuttgart/Berlin,
n.d.; Leo van Puyvelde, *"Rubens"*, Paris/Brussels, 1952; Max Rooses, *"L'oeuvre
de P. P. Rubens"*, 5 vols., Antwerp, 1886ff.

THE DUKE OF LERMA (No. 3137). Canvas 2.87 × 2.00 m. Acquired by the Museum
Foundation and the Ministry in 1969.

The duke of Lerma was the powerful minister to Philip III. When Rubens
arrived in Madrid in 1603 on a mission from the court of Mantua, the duke of
Lerma asked him to paint his portrait. He is shown almost en face on a fiery
horse, dressed in armour with the commanding staff of a generalissimo and
the chain of the orden of Santiago. In the background, under a sky with bold
clouds, a battle is going on. To the left, an imposing palmtree underlines the
allegory of fame and firmess of the duke. Portraying a person on horseback en
face was somewhat unusual at the beginning of the 17thC. Rubens did,
however, have several precursors for this portrait, most notably the graphic
representations of battles of the victorious sovereign. This treatment is found
both in Tempestà and in Crispin de Passe. But Rubens is the first to have
elevated the "type" to something monumental, combining the statuary
quality with a dramatic presence.

RUBENS. 1577-1640.

ST. GEORGE AND THE DRAGON (No. 1644). Canvas 3.03 × 2.56 m. In 1774 in El Pardo.

It was among the state of Rubens' property, executed, however, during his years in Italy, between 1606 and 1608. Michael Jaffé has surmised that it was originally intended for an altar in Genoa. The dramatic composition with the horse rising on its hind legs and the knight about to strike the blow depends iconographically on Italian images with the same subject. As far as the formal is concerned, the impuls was mainly given by Leonardos sketches of horses and riders.

RUBENS. 1577-1640.

THE ADORATION OF THE MAGI (No. 1638). Canvas 3.46 × 4.88 m. Formerly in the Alcázar in Madrid.

Commissioned by the Antwerp municipal government. The gilt frame was paid in 1609. The last instalment was paid to Rubens en 1611. In 1612 the city government gave the painting to the Spanish diplomat, Count de Oliva. In 1629, during his stay in Madrid, Rubens enlarged the painting on the right hand side and on the top and made slight alterations. A drawing in Groningen shows the original size. Among the numerous Adorations of the Magi carried out by Rubens this is the only one not intended for an altar. Rubens could, therefore, choose a broad canvas and display the pomp of the oriental robes, the carriers, and the animals in all their abundance. The first version was probably a night painting. Rubens lightened it up in 1629.

RUBENS. 1577-1640.

PHILIP II ON HORSEBACK (No. 1686). Canvas 3.14 × 2.28 m.

In 1628, during his second stay in Madrid, Rubens painted a portrait of Philip IV on horseback which burned in the 18thC. This equestrian portrait of Philip II must have formed a pair with the lost portrait. We see the King ir armour and with the baton of a commander. Victory holds a laurel wreath above his head. The battle scene in the background are said to be the battle of Sain Quentin in 1557. There are reminiscences of Titian in the figure of the king (see particularly No. 411, Prado).

RUBENS. 1577-1640.

THE GARDEN OF LOVE (No. 1690). Canvas 1.98 × 2.83 m.

This is Rubens' most magnificent painting in the Prado Museum. The rich orchestration of colour with silver and black, profound shades of greens and blues is truly brilliant, fresher than Rubens' usual colours. A choice and at the same time sublime note defines dresses and architecture. The painting was originally called "Conversatie à la mode", is, therefore, a social gathering scene. The cupids mingle with groups of walkers, seated people, and the couple with the lute playing and singing. They scatter flowers and shoot arrows of love, bring torches and crowns and pairs of doves and yokes, symbols of matrimony. It might be Venus riding a dolphin on the fountain while next to her is a peacock, attribute of Juno, the protector of matrimony and motherhood. Inside the palace we see the Graces, distributing beauty and harmony. The painting seems to depict a happy marriage feast joined by the Graces, by Venus, and Juno/Lucina who promises children. There is a personal vein in the imposing composition: Rubens who had been widowed since 1626 remarried in 1630. The garden of love was painted between 1632 and 1634. One has tried to recognize Rubens and Helen Fourment in the couple to the left. This painting was kept by Rubens until his death.

RUBENS. 1577-1640.

THE CARDINAL INFANTE DON FERNANDO AT THE BATTLE OF NÖRDLINGEN (No. 1687). Canvas 3.35 × 2.28 m.

Don Fernando is seen on horseback dressed in shining armour with the baton of a commander and a red sash. Under a cloudy sky in the background the furious battle is going on. The imperial eagle rushes down over the Cardinal-Infante's head. Next to it a genius throws a bundle of lightnings against the enemy. The sonorous inscription denotes the prince as the lightning of divine revenge putting the enemies of the Holy Roman Empire to flight. The painting was probably not done exclusively by Rubens. It must have been carried out soon after the battle of Nördlingen (1634).

RUBENS. 1577-1640.

THE THREE GRACES (No. 1670). Wooden panel 2.21 × 1.81 m.

The composition goes back to an antique group which has been handed down to us through marble statues in Siena and frequently on gems. Rubens has changed the model into sensual figures with exuberant forms of completely heterodox proportions. The blue of the sky increases the effect of the light, blond incarnate and the festive, serene appearance. The main figures were painted by Rubens, in the details participated his assistants. The painting, done after 1635, was in the artist's estate.

RUBENS. 1577-1640.

ATALANTA AND MELEAGER HUNTING THE BOAR IN CALYDONIA (No. 1662). Canvas 1.60 × 2.60 m.

This may well be the landscape with the same subject listed in Rubens' estate. The boar is coursed by the dogs at the edge of a bog in a forest with high trees. To the left Atalanta is kneeling on a fallen trunk, still holding her bow, the arrow sticks behind the boar's ear. From the sides the rest of the hunters from Ovid's story are approaching on foot and on horseback. The painting in thick oil coulours is from Rubens' last years and is considered today, against Max Rooses' doubt as a work from the artist's own hand.

RUBENS. 1577-1640.

THE HOLY FAMILY (No. 1640). Wooden panel 0.87 × 1.25 m.

Mary, with the sleeping child in her arms, is seated in front of a rose bush, angels are flying about. Next to her are two female saints and St. George in armour with the flag, and the dragon at his feet. To the right one glimpses Joseph in the evening landscape. He is resting under a tree together with the donkey. Led by angels St. John the child approaches with the lamb. Various subjects are treated here: Rest on the Flight into Egypt; the Sacra Conversazione; and an allusion to the Passion of Jesus, as well as the Salvation. The precious painting, done entirely by Rubens probably after 1635, was part of his estate.

RUBENS. 1577-1640.

THE VILLAGERS' DANCE (No. 1691). Wooden panel 0.73 × 1.01 m. In Rubens' estate this painting was called "dans van Italiaensche boeren".

The subject stems from a Flemish tradition which has here been treated with a southern-antique colouring. The shawm's music comes from the tree in the center. Two couples form arches by stretching cloths through which the gay chain of dancers passes. The house with its open porch is in Italian style. The golden afternoon landscape is Flemish. The outfits vary, some are contemporary, and others have bacchic motivs. Thus, this pause of farmers changes to a pastoral scene which seems to anticipate the French "Fêtes Galantes" of the 18thC. The painting is from Rubens' last years.

PAUL DE VOS. About 1596-1678.
Born in Hulst, active in Antwerp. Along with the elder Snyders who was married to the sister of Vos, the belonged to the circle of Antwerp painters dealing with hunting subjects on large size canvas'. Paintings like the present once occupied a large number of rooms in the Spanish royal palaces. Especially Philip IV was a passionate hunter.

BULL OVERCOME BY DOGS (No. 1872). Canvas 1.57 × 2.00 m. Also this painting comes from the Torre de la Parada.

JACOB FOPENS VAN ES, about 1596-1666. Flemish School.

STILL-LIFE (No. 1505). Wooden panel 0.27 × 0.32 m.

ANTON VAN DYCK. 1599-1641.

Van Dyck's creative life is divided into four periods. The first in Antwerp (1617-1621), where he was Rubens' assistant from 1617 to 1620. In 1621 he went to England. 1622-27 in Italy, active mainly in Genoa. 1628-32 in Antwerp may be considered his master years. During his last years in London court painter for Charles I. This period was interrupted by travels to Antwerp, The Hague, and Paris. Lit.: Glück, *"Des Meisters Gemälde"*, 1931[2].

THE THORN CORONATION (No. 1474). Canvas 2.23 × 1.96 m. A gift from van Dyck to Rubens, from whose estate it was probably acquired for Philip IV in 1640. This altar piece, with characteristic modifications following a Titian composition now in the Louvre, belongs to the first Antwerp period. Lit.: Glück, p. 49.

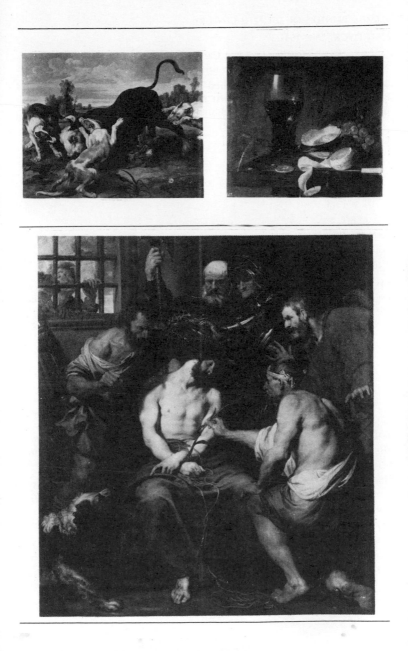

VAN DYCK. 1599-1641.

COUNT HENRY DE BERGH (No. 1486). Canvas 1.14 × 1.00 m. Signed: A. VA. DYK F. Not mentioned in the royal inventory until 1794.

Bergh, born in Bremen in 1573, died en 1638; he was the brother-in-law of Maurice of Nassau. He fought first for and later against Spain. Van Dyck painted his portrait between 1629 and 1632, after his journey to Italy.

VAN DYCK. 1599-1641.

THE ONE-HANDED PAINTER MARTIN RYCKAERT (No. 1479). Wooden panel 1.48 × 1.13 m. In 1666 in the Alcázar in Madrid.

Ryckaert (1587-1631) belonged to the artist's circle of friends. This magnificent portrait must have been painted during van Dyck's second period in Antwerp, after 1627 and before 1631. Lit.: Glück, p. 332.

VAN DYCK. 1599-1641.

THE ORGANIST HENRY LIBERTI (No. 1490). Canvas 1.07 × 0.97 m. The portrait is listed in the 1818 Palace inventory.

Liberti (1600-1661) was organist at the Antwerp cathedral. There are various replicas of the painting which was done between 1627 and 1632. The best is in Munich. Lit.: Glück, p. 330.

THE ENGRAVER PAUL DU PONT (?) (No. 1488). Canvas 1.12 × 1.00 m. in the 1795 inventory in the villa of the duke of Arco.

Painted between 1627 and 1632. The identificacion of Paul du Pont is probable, but not certain.

DAVID TENIERS II "THE YOUNGER". 1610-1690.

Born in Antwerp. Apprenticed to his father and friend of Rubens. From 1651 to 1656 court painter and director of Archduke Leopold Wilhelm of Austria's art collection in Brussels. Lit.: S. Speth-Holterhoff, *"Les Peintres Flamands de Gabinets d'Amateurs au XVII siècle"*, Paris-Brussels, 1957.

ARCHDUKE LEOPOLD IN HIS GALLERY IN BRUSSELS (No. 1813). Copper 1.06 × × 1.29 m. Signed: David Teniers F. In 1666 in the Alcázar in Madrid.

As director of the Archduke's picture gallery, Teniers had inventoried his master's collection of famous works, today in Vienna, Munich, and Madrid. We see the Prince and Teniers himself among well-known paintings by Raphael, Titian, Palma, Giorgione, Van Dyck and others, today in Vienna.

TENIERS II. 1610-1690.

VILLAGE FESTIVAL (No. 1785). Copper 0.69 × 0.86 m. Signed: David Teniers Fec. Acquired by Charles IV.

The small masterpiece shows distinguished people visiting a popular festival in front of an inn.

DUTCH PAINTERS FROM THE 17TH CENTURY

W. BRAUNFELS

The works of the great century of the independent Dutch provinces did not belong to the collecting scope of the Hapsburg monarchy. One did not esteem, neither in the Escorial nor in Madrid or in Vienna, this non-aristocratic art of a people who did not paint sacred or mythological topics but landscapes, citizens, farmers, grazing cattle, and ships on the sea. While there were almost eighty paintings by Rubens in the royal collections, there was not a single one by Rembrandt in the 17thC, and still today there is none by Frans Hals, Vermeer van Delft, or Jan Steen. Only because Rafael Mengs intervened did Charles IV buy the first Rembrandt, No. 2131. At the same time the first paintings by Ostade and Ruysdael were bought. The collection remained small. In the last few decades the Museum has had some opportunities: in 1944 they obtained Rembrandt's late self portrait and a landscape by Hobbema. The void could never be filled completely. It testifies to a historical reality of a particular magnitude.

REMBRANDT HARMENSZ VAN RYN. 1606-1669.

Born in Leyden. From 1630 until his death active in Amsterdam. Lit.: A. Bredius (Revised by Gerson), "Complete Edition of the Paintings", London, 1969.

ARTEMISIA (No. 2132). Canvas 1.42 × 1.53 m. Signed: Rembrant f. 1634. Acquired in 1769 for Charles IV through the intervention of Mengs.

It is not certain that it shows Artemisia being served by a young girl offering her wine with the ashes of her husband Mausolus. Expression, posture, and the cup itself tell us that it may also be Sophonisbe who is being served the cup of poison. In either case the princess symbolizes marital fidelity. Saskia who had married Rembrandt the same year (1634) acted as model. Lit.: Bredius-Gerson No. 379.

REMBRANDT. 1606-1669.

SELF-PORTRAIT (No. 2808). Canvas 0.81 × 0.65 m. Acquired in 1944 from a Spanish collector. It shows Rembrandt at the age of 58. It is similar in expression and posture to two other self portraits: the one from 1660 in the Louvre, the other from about 1663 in Lord Iveagh's collection in London. Bredius, Bauch, and Gerson do not include this one as authentic in their catalogues of Rembrandt's complete works.

PHIPLIS WOUWERMAN. 1619-1668.

Born and died in Harlem. He was one of the favorite Dutch painters at the Spanish court in the 18thC. His speciality were hunting scenes, battles, and scenes with soldiers in open landscape.

DEPARTURE FOR THE HUNT (No. 2150). Canvas 0.80 × 0.70 m. Signed: PHLS W. Also this painting may have been in La Granja in 1746.

JACOB VAN RUYSDAEL. 1628-1682.

Active in Amsterdam. Lit.: J. Rosenberg, *"Jacob van Ruysdael"*, Berlin, 1928.

OAK FORREST (No. 1728). Panel 0.55 × 0.61 m. Acquired along with No. 1729 for Charles IV.

RUYSDAEL. 1628-1682.

LANDSCAPE (No. 1729). Panel 0.61 × 0.61 m. Signed: J. V. Ruysdael fc. Acquired for Charles IV.

It has been said of Ruysdael that he painted the tragedy of nature, mostly fantasy landscapes, the composition of which is full of pathos and seriousness. This oak forest with a thunderstorm is a characteristic piece from the sixties.

GABRIEL METSU. 1629-1667.

Born and died in Leyden.

DEAD ROOSTER (No. 2103). Panel 0.57 × 0.40 m. Signed: G. Metsu. In Charles IV's collection.

Metsu painted very few still-lives. He is a very delicate painter depicting interiors of middle-class life. Nevertheless, this painting shows clearly the accuracy and refinement with which he treated both structures and the plumage of the rooster.

MEINDERT HOBBEMA. 1638-1709.
Born and died in Amsterdam.

LANDSCAPE (No. 2860). Panel 0.42 × 0.56 m. Signed: M. Hobbema. Acquired in 1844.

ENGLISH AND FRENCH PAINTING

W. BRAUNFELS

The great period in English painting (1750-1850) was not represented in the Spanish royal palaces and collections. Only in the past twenty years great efforts have been made to form a small nucleus of English painting, thus introducing a considerable change of the total panorama of "European painting" in accordance with more recent insights of art history.

French painting from the 16th and 17thC as well as the 18thC was not within the collecting scope of the Spanis crown.

This state of affairs did not change when, with Philip V, the Bourbons took over from the Hapsburgs. Most acquisitions were single pieces, mainly portraits coming from the royal houses allied to them by marriage.

It is true that Philip IV had ordered a series of paintings from Claude Lorrain. Philip V succeeded in acquiring some magnificent paintings by Poussin, and Isabel de Farnesio the two Watteau's, but not at any time did the monarchs feel themselves stimulated, as in the case of Flemish and Italian painting, to complete or round off their collection of French paintings. This, above all, is a characteristic element of the cultural politics of the Bourbons in the 18thC.

SIR JOSHUA REYNOLDS.
Born in Plympton-Earl's in 1723 and died in London in 1792.

PORTRAIT OF A CLERGY (No. 2858). Canvas 0.77 × 0.64 m. Acquired in 1943

GEORGE ROMNEY. 1734-1802.

PORTRAIT OF MASTER WARD (No. 3013). Canvas 1.26 × 1.02 m. Acquired by the Museum in 1958.

The portrait of the young Ward in an English park remained until 1931 in Ward's family at Charlton House near Canterbury. The natural relaxation of the posture conforms to the ideal of life for the upper class in the second half of the 18thC in England.

THOMAS GAINSBOROUGH. 1727-1788.
Gainsborough is among the oldest masters of great quality who, between 1750 and 1850, brought the English School to its prime. Nex to few landscapes, his portraits are the center of his production.

DOCTOR ISAAC HENRIQUE SEQUEIRA (No. 2979). Canvas 1.27 × 1.02 m. Legacy of Bertram Newhouse, 1953.

The doctor was descended from a Portuguese Jewish family. He studied medicine in Leyden and died old-aged in London in 1816. The portrait is a late work by Gainsborough.

NICOLAS POUSSIN. 1594-1665.

Born in Les Andelys in Normandy. From 1624 until his death he lived in Rome with the exception of a journey to Paris 1641-42. After Velázquez, Rembrandt, and Rubens, Poussin was one of the most important painters of the 17thC. Lit.: Anthony Blunt, "Painting of Nicolas Poussin", London, 1966; Kurt Badt, "Die Kunst des Nicolas Poussin", Cologne, 1969.

THE PARNASSUS (No. 2313). Canvas 1.45 × 1.97 m. From Philip V's collection. 1746 in La Granja.

A major work from Poussin's first period, about 1730. Apollo is offering a drink from the spring of Castalia to a poet (according to Panofsky this poet is Poussin's sponsor, Marino). Calliope passes him the two crowns of present fame and of inmortality. From the trees putti break off laurel branches which the poets in the foreground wear as head adornments. Lit.: Blunt No. 129; Badt, p. 527.

POUSSIN. 1594-1665.

MELEAGER'S HUNT (No. 2320). Canvas 1.60 × 3.60 m. Already in 1701 mentioned in the Retiro.

It shows Meleager's hunt with Atalanta according to Ovid's Metamorphoses (VII 298ff). The size of the canvas, unusual for Poussin, as well as the narrative style have given rise to doubts about the painting's authenticity. Blunt (No. 163) has laid those doubts to rest.

CLAUDE LORRAIN: 1600-1682.
Claude Gellée, called Le Lorrain, was born in Chamagne in the Vosges. Since 1613 he lived almost without interruptions in Rome. Lit.: M. Rüthlisberger, "Claude Lorrain, The Paintings, Critical Catalogue", New Haven, 1961.
LANDSCAPE WITH ST. PAULA THE ROMAN EMBARKING IN OSTIA (No. 2254). Canvas 2.11 × 1.45 m.

Contemporary companion piece to Nos. 2252 and 2253. The architecture scenery is characteristic of Claude Lorrain who combines antique and baroque forms. Equally characteristic are his boats. Lorrain's paintings almost always show sunlight filtering through haze in the background. Lit.: Röthlisberger, No. 49.

PHILIPPE DE CHAMPAIGNE. 1602-1674.
Born in Brussels and died in Paris.

LOUIS XIII OF FRANCE (No. 2240). Canvas 1.08 × 0.86 m.

Louis XIII was born in 1601, in 1615 married to Anna of Austria, Philip III of Spain's daughter. He died in 1643. The painting is to have carried the signature: Champagne fecit 1655 (sic).

PIERRE GOBERT. 1662-1744.
Born in Fontainebleau, died in Paris.

LOUIS XV AS A CHILD (No. 2262). Canvas 1.29 × 0.98

Louis XV was the son of the duke of Burgundy and Maria Adelaide of Savoy. He was born in 1710, became king in 1715, and died in 1774. The picture, dated 1714, shows the child four years old.

JEAN ANTOINE WATTEAU. 1684-1721.
Born in Valenciennes. He worked mainly in Paris; since 1717 member of the Académie Royal. Lit.: H. Adhémar, "Watteau", Paris, 1950.

MARRIAGE CONTRACT AND PEASANT DANCE (No. 2353). Canvas 0.47 × 0.55 m. Since 1746 listed in Isabel de Farnesio's collection in La Granja. Companion to No. 2354. Lit.: Adhémar No. 134.

WATTEAU. 1684-1721.

FESTIVAL IN A PARK (No. 2354). Canvas 0.48 × 0.56 m. Companion to No. 2353. Lit.: Adhémar No. 135.

COURT PAINTERS IN MADRID: FLEMISH, ITALIANS, AND GERMANS

W. BRAUNFELS.

Portraits of the kings of Spain, of their families, and of the great men at the court were always important in the decoration of the Spanish Royal Palaces. Replicas of such paintings were frequently sent to the courts in Vienna, Paris, and Naples. From these courts portraits came in return presents to Madrid. This tradition began with the portraits Titian furnished to Charles V. The most important of the later court painters were Spaniards: namely Velázquez for Philip IV and Goya for Charles IV. Meanwhile, foreign painters were ordered by the Madrid Court to portray the royal families: the Dutch Anton Mor by Philip II, French like van Loo, Ranc and others for Philip V, and Mengs for Charles III and the young Charles IV.

These court paintings form a group in themselves. They are bes appreciated if looked at separately from the rest of the Flemish, French, and German works. One of their characteristics in the technical perfection with which they were painted.

ANTHONIS MOR (ANTONIO MORO). Between 1517/20-1576.
Born in Utrecht, died in Antwerp. After a stay in Rome court painter in Lisbon and Madrid under Philip II. 1553-54 in London by orders of the King.

MARIA OF AUSTRIA, WIFE OF EMPEROR MAXIMILIAN II. Signed: Antonius Mor Pinx. Ano 1551. Since 1600 in the Alcázar.

EMPEROR MAXIMILIAN II (No. 2111). The painting forms a pair with No. 2110. Signed: Mor Pinxit 1550. Canvas 1.81 × 0.90 m. and 1.84 × 1.00 m.

Mary of Austria (1528-1603), daughter of Charles V and sister of Philip II, married in 1548 her cousin Maximilian (1527-1576) who in 1564 was elected Emperor. Emperor Maximilian born in Vienna in 1527, was the nephew of Charles V and son of Ferdinand I. In 1564 he was elected emperor to succeed his father. He died in 1576. Mor is in this portrait following a model by Titian.

ANTHONIS MOR (ANTONIO MORO). Between 1517/20-1576.

PEJERON, JESTER TO THE COUNT OF BENAVENTE AND TO THE DUKE OF ALBA (No. 2107). Wooden panel 1.81 × 0.92 m. Since 1600 in the inventories of the Alcázar in Madrid.

Not only were jesters found at all courts of the 16thC and 17thC, but the portraits of these renowned persons are in the castles' inventories. Still, this full-length portrait may be the oldest preserved of a jester.

MOR. Between 1517/20-1576.

MARY TUDOR, QUEEN OF ENGLAND, SECOND WIFE OF PHILIP II OF SPAIN (No. 2108). Wooden panel 1.09 × 0.84 m. Signed: Antonius Mor pingebat 1554. In Charles V's collection in Yuste.

The marriage between the Spanish heir and catholic, old Mary Tudor of England (daughter of Henry VIII, married 1554, died 1558) was based on Charles V's plan to unite the two maritime powers. The death of the queen led history on a different course.

MOR. Between 1517/20-1576.

CATHERINE OF AUSTRIA, WIFE OF JUAN III OF PORTUGAL (No. 2109). Wooden panel 1.07 × 0.84 m. Painted in 1552. Since 1600 in the Alcázar in Madrid. Catherine (1507-1578) was the youngest sister of Charles V. In 1525 she married Juan III of Portugal (1502-1557), organizer of the Brazil colony.

LADY WITH A TRINKET (No. 2113). Wooden panel 1.07 × 0.83 m. Acquired by Charles III. Attempts to identify the lady have so far not been successful.

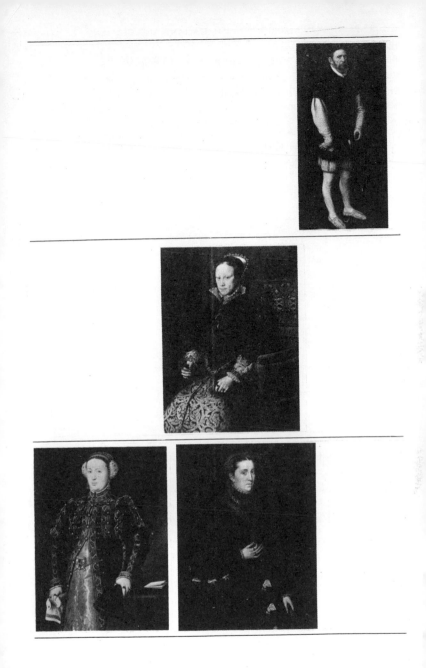

JEAN RANC. 1674-1735.

Born in Montpellier. 1722-35 court painter of Philip V.

PHILIP V'S FAMILY (No. 2376). Canvas 0.44 × 0.65 m.

The painting must have been executed right after the artist's arrival in Madrid, September 1722. It shows the presentation of the portrait of Luisa Isabel of Orleans (1709-1742) to her Husband, Hereditary Prince Luis I (1707-1724). Seated: Philip V, his second wife Isabel de Farnesio, and the three younger sons: Fernando (1713-1759), king 1746; Philip (1720-1785); and Charles (1716-1788), king of Spain as of 1759.

MICHELE-ANGE HOUASSE. 1680-1730.

Born in Paris. Before 1717 court painter to Philip V. Died in 1730.

LUIS I (No. 2387). Canvas 1.72 × 1.12 m.

The inscription below reads: Luis de Bourbon, Prince des Asturies Age dix ans le mois d'aoust 1717. Luis I, son of Philip V and Maria Luis Gabriela of Savoy, was born in 1707, anointed king in 1724, the year of his death.

LOUIS MICHEL VAN LOO. 1707-1771.

Born in Toulon. In 1733 member of the Académie Royale. Court painter to Philip V. When the King died, van Loo returned to Paris.

PHILIP V'S FAMILY (No. 2283). Canvas 4.16 × 5.11 m. Signed: L. M. van Loo 1743.

It is one of the largest "official" paintings of the Spanish crown. Its commission was van Loo's motive for travelling to Madrid. The technical exuberance and the care which the artist dedicated to this painting corredpond to the political significance of the persons represented.

From left to right: Maria Antonia Victoria (1718-1781), married to king Joseph I of Portugal; Barbara of Braganza (1711-1759), married to Ferdinand VI; Prince Ferdinand (1713-1759), since 1746 king of Spain; Philip V (1683-1746), king of Spain since 1700; cardinal-infante Luis (1727-1785); Isabel de Farnesio (1692-1766), queen of Spain since 1714; Philip, duke of Parma (1720-1765); Louise Isabelle of France (1727-1759), daughter of Louis VI, married to Philip, duke of Parma; Maria Teresa Antonia (1726-1746), married to the son of Louis XV; Maria Antonia Fernanda (1729-1785); Maria Amalia of Saxony (1724-1760), daughter of August II of Saxony, married to Charles III; Charles (1716-1788), king of Naples in 1738, and of Spain in 1759; in front, playing with a dog: Isabel Maria Luisa (1741-1763), daughter of the duke of Parma; Maria Isabel (1743-1749), daughter of Charles III.

ANTON RAPHAEL MENGS. 1728-1779.

Born in Aussig (Bohemia). In 1741 in Rome. Since 1745 court painter in Dresden. In Madrid 1761-69 and 1774-76.

Lit.: F. J. Sánchez Cantón, *"A. R. Mengs, 1728-1779"*, Madrid, 1929. D. Honisch, *"A. R. Mengs"*, Recklinghausen, 1965.

MARIA JOSEPHA OF LOTHRINGEN, ARCHDUCHESS OF AUSTRIA (No. 2186). Canvas 1.28 × 0.98 m.

Maria Josefa was the daughter of Emperor Francis I and Maria Theresa. She was engaged to Ferdinand VI of Spain but died before the marriage could take place. In this portrait as well as in the others which he painted for the court, Mengs strove for a perfect technique and style, close to the Rococo of the court. The same may be said of his religious compositions. Age and history of Maria Josefa allows us to date this portrait to 1767-68.

THE PRADO MUSEUM

P. LOPEZ DE OSABA

On November 9, 1818, after a stormy history, the doors were opened to the Madrid Museum, one month after the third wedding of King Ferdinand VII. On October 20 he had married Maria Amalia of Saxony. But the idea for the Museum was conceived much earlier.

Foremost among the reforms carried out during the reign of Charles III is the development of the Paseo del Prado in Madrid, the famous water-course, a place for outings, walks, and meeting friends. It was originally divided into two areas, El Prado de San Jerónimo, and El Prado de Atocha, named after the two famous convent.

The project for the development was entrusted to the architect Ventura Rodríguez in 1767, while the count of Aranda, a man of the Enlightenment and of great culture, was minister of state. Thus appear the first gardens and fountains of the great public avenue. Facing the western facade of the Convent of San Jeronimo, next to the Botanical Gardens, a space was set aside for the Museum of Natural Sciences. The year was 1785 and Floridablanca was by then minister of state.

The final project was presented by Juan de Villanueva, the son of the sculptor and the brother of the other architect, Diego. Juan de Villanueva is the great figure in Spanish classicist architecture of the 18th Century.

He was born in 1739. Twenty years old he went to Rome where his artistic sense was heightened by the contact with the great masterpieces from all periods, the supreme testimonies of the art and genius of their authors. Later, while Villanueva worked in the Escorial, Juan de Herrera's mastery influenced him, from a distance, with its lesson of monumentality and austerity.

The perfect mixture of Spanish tradition and classical inspiration makes the Museum the best and most succesful work by Villanueva.

The Museum was almost finished in 1808, that year of sad memory for Spain, her monuments and art works. Vaults, lead roofs, etc., were ready when the French occupational forces requisitioned the building and turned it into horse stables.

After the lead was wrenched off the roofs, the building was left exposed to the elements and fell into ruin. The reconstruction carried out after the occupation is only a pale reflection of what Villanueva had planned, due to the indigent state of Spanish economy after the disastrous war.

When the conflict was over, one returned to the idea proposed already by Joseph Bonaparte of restoring and adapting the Buenavista Palace for a museum of paintings. However, this large undertaking, which was begun by the duchess of Alba, required a lot of money for its fulfillment, and it never prospered. The proposal was then made to Ferdinand VII to finish the Villanueva building as a Museum of Paintings.

Traditionally, doña Isabel de Braganza, King Ferdinand's second wife, has been considered the principal promoter of the creation of the Museum. The exaggeration of this assertion has been more than demonstrated by Pedro Beroquí and Sánchez Cantón. In 1818, in the face of the deplorable state of Spanish finances, the King personally took charge of the construction of the Museum. He included his wife in the enterprise, but a few months later the queen died. The work was hurried along to be finished in time to commemorate the third royal wedding.

The last details were entrusted to the Court painter Vicente López, as advisor, and the marquis of Santa Cruz, the King's representative. When the public visited the Museum for the first time, there were 311 paintings hanging on the walls of the picture gallery.

The painter Luis Eusebi was appointed curator. He edited the first catalogue with 21 pages and printed by the Royal Press en 1819.

With the appointment in 1820 of the prince of Anglona, a member of the ducal house of Osuna, the number of paintings increased: the 1881 catalogue already had 512 items.

Since then the number of paintings has increased considerably. The 1972 catalogue registers 3209 paintings. Both by the number of its paintings and by their very high quality, the Prado is thus one of the finest galleries in the world.

Finally, we must remember that this great collection was once close to being lost forever. This happened when Ferdinand VII died in 1873. There was no law, under absolute monarchy, that established the nation's rights. With the King dead there was doubt about the Patrimony of the Monarchy. All the art works were therefore inventoried as private property that was to be divided between the King's two daughters. Fortunately, a solution was found. Thus, Isabel II compensated her sister in hard cash, thereby saving a most important part of Spanish history and culture.

Not until 1868, when the queen was forced from the thronce, was a new legal situation established. The Museum was nationalized. It would no longer be called the "Royal Museum", but the "National Museum of Painting and Sculpture".

Subsequent reforms were carried out by the architect Jareño in 1882. Access was made to the lower rotunda of the north facade. Jareño also constructed the flight of stairs at the north facade. They were, however, later changed by the architect Pedro de Muguruza who also has successfully arranged later work in the Museum.

The building consists of five sections placed parallel to the great Paseo del Prado. The two side wings, the north Rotunda, which today is the entrance, and the South Palace, are united to the central portico in Tuscan order by two long parts, the upper gallery in Ionic order. The central body is extended at the back of the building in form of an apse or basilica, today the great Velázquez room. This addition was built between 1845 and 1853, while José de Madrazo was director of the Museum. At that time the Museum already contained 949 paintings.

BIBLIOGRAPHY

Chueca Goitia, Fernando: *"La vida y las obras del arquitecto Juan de Villa-
              nueva"*. In collaboration with Carlos de Miguel,
              Madrid, 1942.

Beroquí, D. Pedro: *"El Museo del Prado, notas para su historia"*. I El Museo
              Real, Madrid, 1933.

Madrazo, Mariano: *"Historia del Museo del Prado, 1818-1868"*. Madrid, 1945.

Madrazo, Mariano: *"Historia del Museo del Prado, 1818-1868"*. Madrid, 1945.

Sánchez Cantón, F. J.: *"El Museo del Prado"*, Santander, 1961.

Lafuente Ferrari, E.: *"El Museo del Prado"*, Madrid, 1964.

Gaya Nuño, J. A.: *"Historia del Museo del Prado (1819-1969)"*. Everest, León,
              1969.

E. Pérez Sánchez, A.: *"Pasado, presente y futuro del Museo del Prado"*, Ma-
              drid, 1977.

INDEX OF ARTIST.

GENERAL INDEX